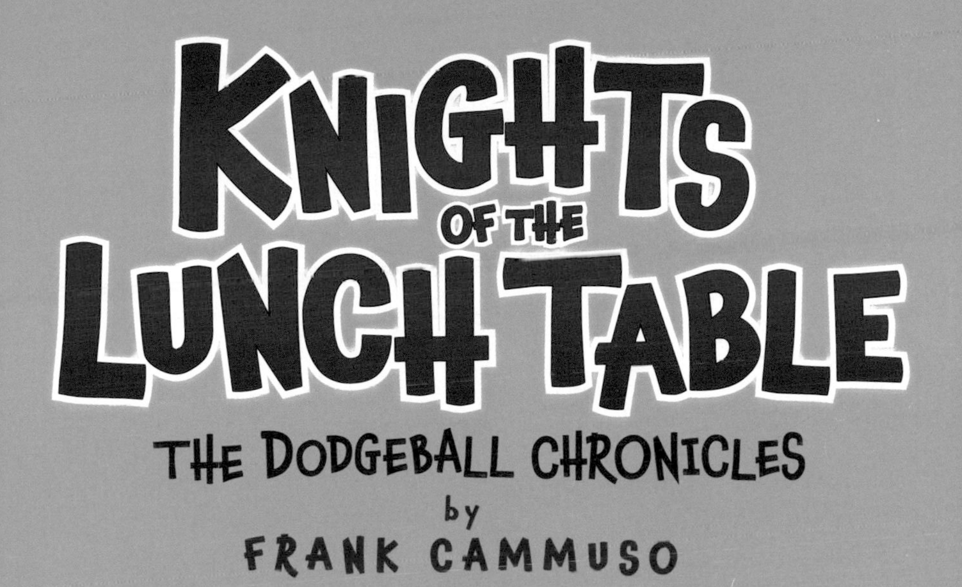

THE DODGEBALL CHRONICLES

by

FRANK CAMMUSO

AN IMPRINT OF

SCHOLASTIC

New York Toronto London Auckland Sydney Mexico City New Delhi Hong Kong Buenos Aires

This book is for anyone who has ever been picked last.
– FC

Special thanks to Ngoc Huynh, Hart Seely, Phil McAndrew, Peter Allen, Tom Peyer, Michael Cho, Bruce Coville, Michael and Harrison Jantze, Sheila Keenan, Phil Falco, Janna Morishima, David Saylor, David McCormick, all the fine folks at *The Post-Standard* and especially the students, faculty, and staff of Durgee Junior High School.

Library of Congress Cataloging-in-Publication Data

Cammuso, Frank.
The dodgeball chronicles / by Frank Cammuso. – 1st ed.
p. cm. – (Knights of the lunch table ; 1)
ISBN-13: 978-0-439-90322-6 (alk. paper)
ISBN-10: 0-439-90322-X (alk. paper)
1. Graphic novel. I. Title.
PN6727.C28D63 2008
741.5'973–dc22
2007037480

10 9 8 7 6 5 4 3 2 08 09 10

First edition, July 2008

Edited by Sheila Keenan
Creative Director: David Saylor
Book design by Phil Falco
Lettering by John Green
Printed in the U.S.A.

NO! I DON'T WANT TO!
COME BACK HERE, YOU LITTLE WIMP!
BEHIND ME, IT'S . . .
THWAK
WHAM
OOOF!
NOBODY ESCAPES ME!

NOBODY ESCAPES DODGEBALL!
WHAT DO YOU WANT?
WHERE IS IT, WART BOY?
WHERE IS MY DIARY?
WHAT?

WAKE UP, *WARTIE! GIVE IT BACK!*
AAAAH! A MONSTER!
ARTHUR! MORGAN! WHAT IS GOING ON IN HERE?
WART BOY STOLE MY DIARY AND WON'T GIVE IT BACK!
THAT'S NOT TRUE!
IT PROBABLY GOT LOST IN THE MOVE!
LIAR! HE'S ALWAYS IN MY ROOM!
MORGAN, *I'LL* HANDLE THIS. GO GET READY FOR SCHOOL.
HMMF, YOU ALWAYS TAKE *HIS* SIDE.

I DON'T HAVE HER DUMB DIARY.
I KNOW YOU DON'T.
MY STOMACH HURTS. CAN I STAY HOME?
IT'S JUST BUTTERFLIES. BESIDES, YOU CAN'T MISS YOUR FIRST DAY AT THE NEW SCHOOL.
WHY DID WE HAVE TO MOVE? WHAT IF THE NEW KIDS DON'T LIKE ME? WHAT IF THEY FIND OUT I *STINK AT SPORTS*? WHAT IF MY LOCKER DOESN'T OPEN? WHAT IF. . .
ARTIE, CALM DOWN.
VALIANT BLADE

YOU DON'T. . .
YES I DO! I STINK AT BASEBALL, FOOTBALL AND DODGEBALL! I STINK AT EVERYTHING! ALL I WANT IS TO BE GOOD AT SOMETHING! ANYTHING!
YOU ARE GOOD AT THINGS. YOU'RE SMART, CARING AND VERY BRAVE.
WITH THAT COMBINATION YOU CAN SUCCEED AT ANYTHING.
EVEN DODGEBALL?
SURE. YOU COULD BECOME A DODGEBALL LEGEND IF YOU WANT.
REALLY?
REALLY. NOW, HOW ABOUT GETTING UP? THE BUS WILL BE HERE SOON.
YEAH, OK.

THIS WILL TEACH THAT RUNT NOT TO TAKE MY DIARY!
SOAP
DISH
MUSTA
HOT SAUCE
SOUR PICKLE
ENJOY YOUR GRUB, WARTHOG.
WARTIE
ISN'T THAT NICE. MORGAN MADE YOUR LUNCH. WHAT DO YOU SAY?
THANKS . . . FOR NOTHING.
SEE YOU TWO TONIGHT. ARTIE, PLEASE REMEMBER TO TAKE OUT THE TRASH.
YEAH, YEAH.

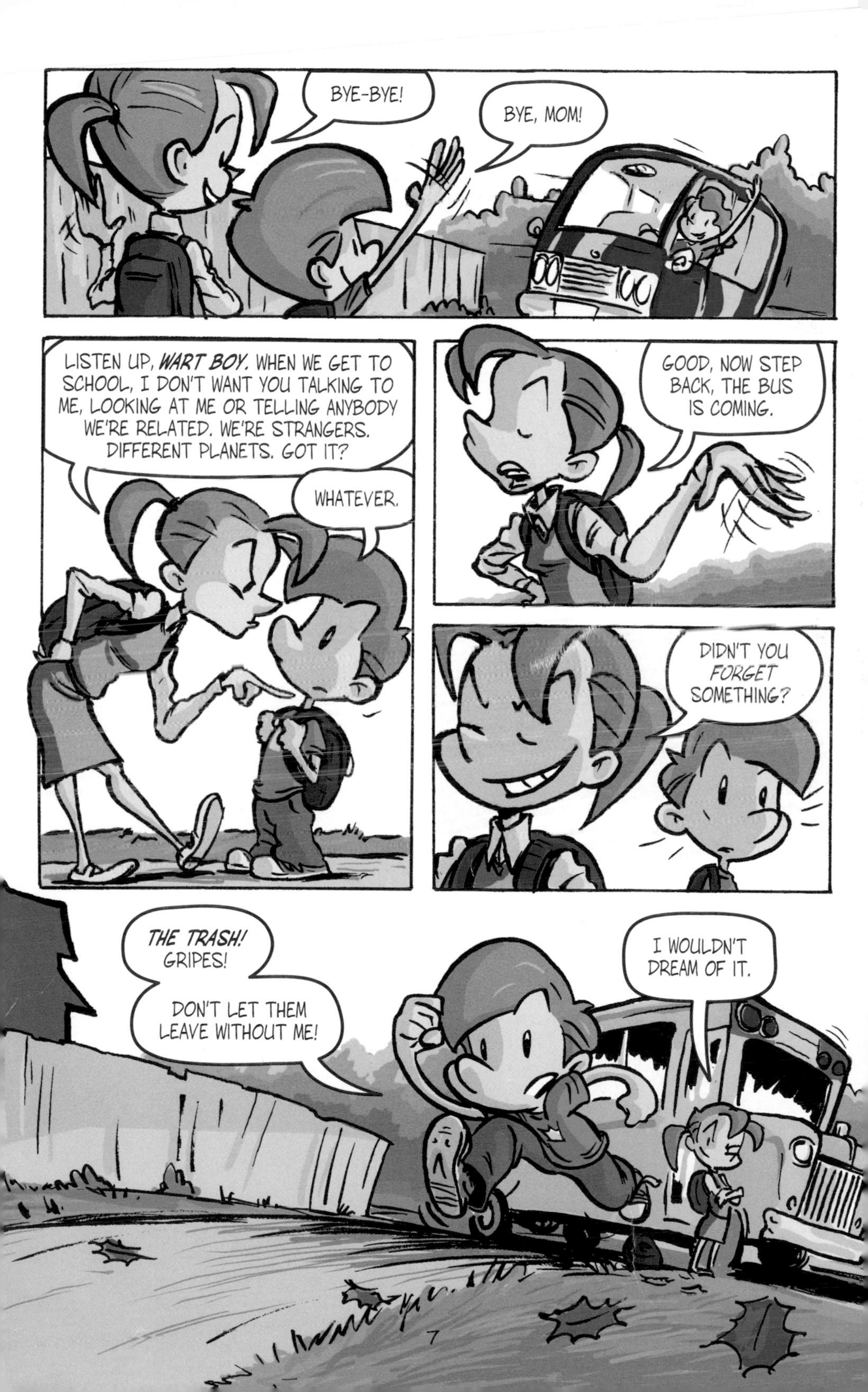
BYE-BYE!
BYE, MOM!
LISTEN UP, WART BOY. WHEN WE GET TO SCHOOL, I DON'T WANT YOU TALKING TO ME, LOOKING AT ME OR TELLING ANYBODY WE'RE RELATED. WE'RE STRANGERS. DIFFERENT PLANETS. GOT IT?
WHATEVER.
GOOD, NOW STEP BACK, THE BUS IS COMING.
DIDN'T YOU FORGET SOMETHING?
THE TRASH! GRIPES!
DON'T LET THEM LEAVE WITHOUT ME!
I WOULDN'T DREAM OF IT.

VROOOM

MISSED THE BUS?
HUH?

DON'T WORRY. BUSES ARE OVERRATED.
TO YOU MAYBE, BUT IT'S MY FIRST DAY AT A NEW SCHOOL.
OH, I SEE. WHAT IF I TOLD YOU I COULD MAGICALLY TRANSPORT YOU THERE?
YOU CAN?
NO, BUT I DO KNOW A SHORTCUT.
FOLLOW THAT PATH THROUGH THE WOODS AND YOU'LL BE TO SCHOOL IN TEN MINUTES.
YOU SURE?
I'M KINDA GOOD AT THIS GUIDANCE STUFF. AS A MATTER OF FACT, HERE'S A PREDICTION FOR YOU: THIS WEEK, YOU SHALL BE TESTED IN WAYS YOU'VE NEVER IMAGINED.
GEE, THANKS.
DON'T MENTION IT. SEE YA!

HOOOWWLL
WHAT'S THAT?!
WHAT'S *HE* DOING?

DID YOU HEAR THAT?
YOU MEAN THE BEAST?
THE WHAT?
THE BEAST! HE LIVES IN THERE.
27
NO WAY. IT'S PROBABLY JUST SOME ANIMAL.
THEY SAY HE'S SEVEN FEET TALL AND HAS THE HEAD OF A SNAKE, THE BODY OF A LION AND FANGS THREE FEET LONG.
REALLY? YOU'VE SEEN THE BEAST?

NO, BUT THIS KID TOMMY MALLORY DID . . . *ONCE.* HE WENT IN THERE BUT *NEVER* CAME OUT. THEY PUT THE BARS UP TO KEEP IT FROM ESCAPING.
REALLY? YOU'RE NOT SCARED?
NAH, I DON'T REALLY BELIEVE IN THE BEAST. MY GUESS IS IT'S A TRAPPED ***BEAR,*** OR MAYBE A ***COUGAR.*** YOU NEVER KNOW WHAT YOU'LL FIND IN THIS WEIRD TOWN.
WHAT WERE YOU DOING HERE?
GETTING LUNCH FOR HANNIBAL. HE LIKES CRICKETS.
HANNIBAL?
HE'S MY *TARANTULA.* WANNA SEE?

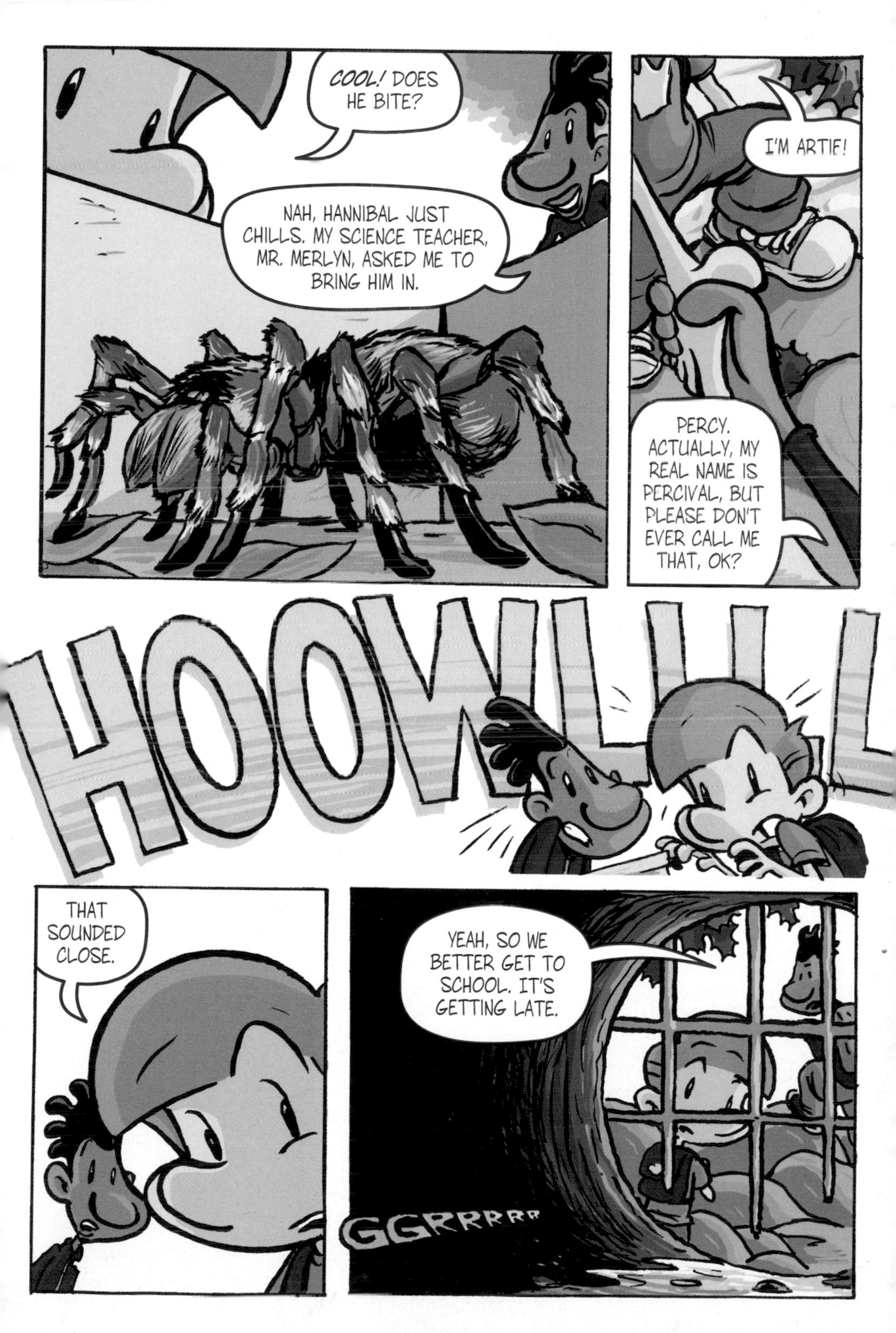
COOL! DOES HE BITE?
NAH, HANNIBAL JUST CHILLS. MY SCIENCE TEACHER, MR. MERLYN, ASKED ME TO BRING HIM IN.
I'M ARTIE!
PERCY. ACTUALLY, MY REAL NAME IS PERCIVAL, BUT PLEASE DON'T EVER CALL ME THAT, OK?
HOOWLLLL
THAT SOUNDED CLOSE.
YEAH, SO WE BETTER GET TO SCHOOL. IT'S GETTING LATE.
GGRRRRRR

WOW!
THIS SCHOOL LOOKS COOL.
COOL? CAMELOT MIDDLE SCHOOL? YOU ARE NEW.
ARTIE?
HOW'D YOU GET HERE SO FAST?
EXCUSE ME, DO I KNOW YOU?
WHO'S THAT?
I DUNNO, SOME STRANGER. MISTAKEN IDENTITY.

CHECK IT OUT! A DODGEBALL!
YEAH, THEY TAKE IT SERIOUSLY AROUND HERE. YOU PLAY?
UH, NO, I MEAN, YEAH.
BACK AT MY OLD SCHOOL, I WAS A DODGEBALL LEGEND. I WAS ALL-STATE, FIRST TEAM.
LUCKY YOU. I HATE DODGEBALL.
YOU DO?
IT'S PROBABLY HARD FOR YOU TO UNDERSTAND, BUT NOT EVERYBODY IS GOOD AT DODGEBALL.
UM, ACTUALLY, I WAS . . .
C'MON, THE COAST IS CLEAR, LET'S GET IN BEFORE THE HORDE SEES US.
THE HORDE? WHAT'S A HORDE?

SEE THOSE GUYS PLAYING DODGEBALL? THAT'S ***THE HORDE.*** THEY PUSH EVERYBODY AROUND. THEY TAKE OUR STUFF. THEY KINDA RULE THE SCHOOL.
C'MON, LET'S . . .
HEY, PERCIVAL, WHAT'S IN YOUR PURSE?
WHATCHA GOT FOR ME TODAY, PERCIVAL?
NOTHING.
IT DOESN'T LOOK LIKE ***NOTHING***, PERCIVAL. YOU KNOW YOU GOTTA GIVE ME ***SOMETHING*** OR YOU CAN'T GET IN.

HERE, YOU CAN HAVE MY LUNCH.
THAT'LL WORK!
LATER, LADIES.
YOU DIDN'T HAVE TO DO THAT.
IT'S OK, MY SISTER PROBABLY SPIT IN IT ANYWAYS.
WHO WAS THAT?
DWAYNE FERRYMAN. HE'S WITH THE HORDE. THOSE JERKS SHAKE ME DOWN EVERY WEEK.
WHY DOESN'T THE PRINCIPAL DO SOMETHING ABOUT THEM?
PRINCIPAL DAGGER? ARE YOU KIDDING? SHE'S ***WORSE.***

PLEASE, OH, PLEASE, MRS. DAGGER, WISE AND POWERFUL QUEEN OF THE SCHOOL. I BEG YOU. PLEASE, I'LL NEVER DO IT AGAIN!
STOP GROVELING, MR. KOZLOWSKI. YOU'RE GETTING SPITTLE ON MY SHOES!
YOU KNOW THE RULES. NO ELECTRONIC DEVICES ON SCHOOL GROUNDS. THANK YOU FOR YOUR DONATION!
BUT IT'S NOT MINE! IT'S MY BROTHER'S!
TOO BAD.
THAT STINKS!
PERHAPS, YOU'D LIKE TO FAMILIARIZE YOURSELF WITH THIS DURING LUNCH PERIOD DETENTION.
Camelot Middle School Rules and Regulations Vol. IX
RULES ARE RULES, MR. KOZLOWSKI. IF WE DIDN'T HAVE RULES, DO YOU KNOW WHAT WE'D HAVE?
FUN?

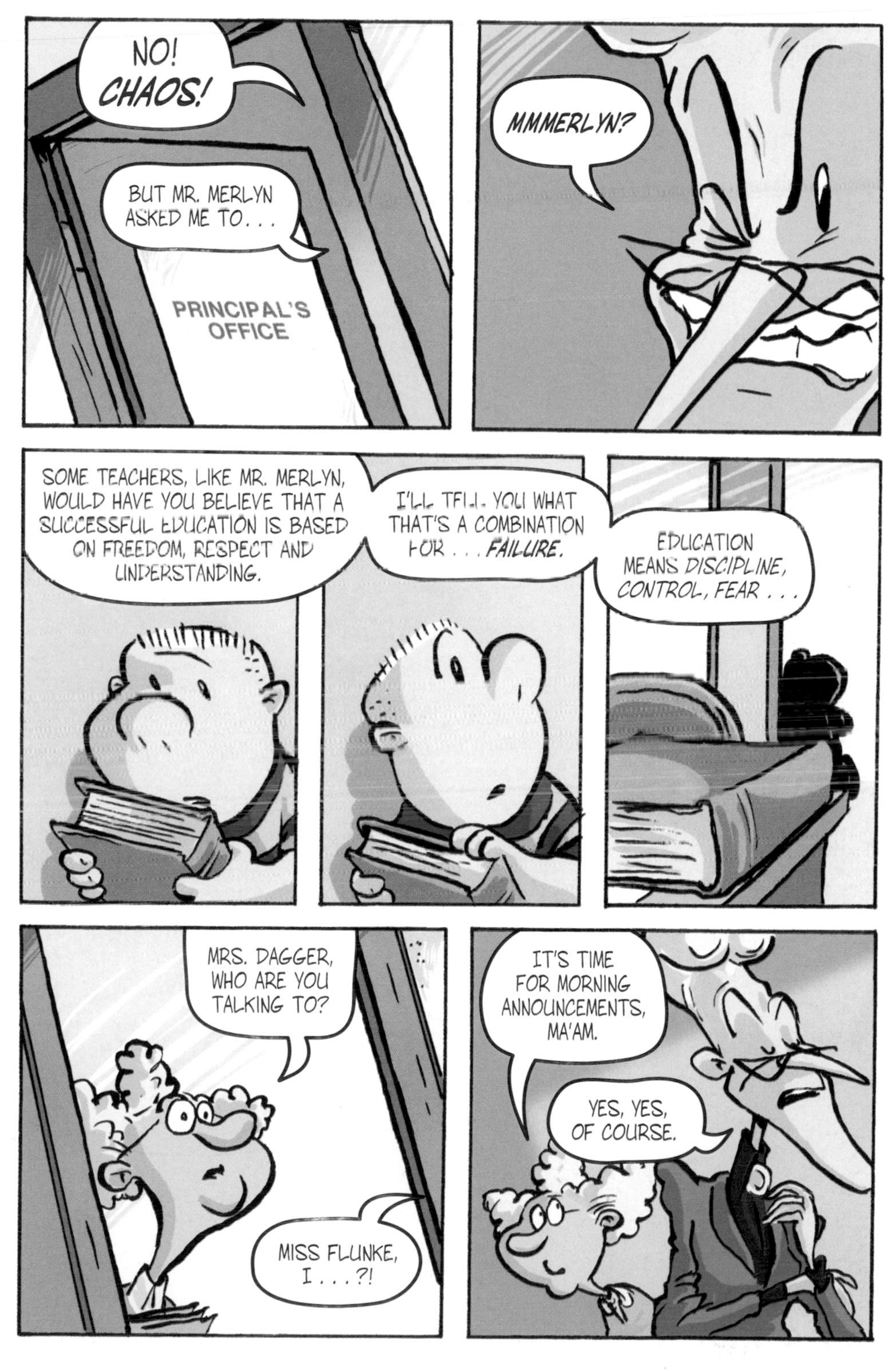
NO! CHAOS!
BUT MR. MERLYN ASKED ME TO . . .
PRINCIPAL'S OFFICE
MMMERLYN?
SOME TEACHERS, LIKE MR. MERLYN, WOULD HAVE YOU BELIEVE THAT A SUCCESSFUL EDUCATION IS BASED ON FREEDOM, RESPECT AND UNDERSTANDING.
I'LL TELL YOU WHAT THAT'S A COMBINATION FOR . . . FAILURE.
EDUCATION MEANS DISCIPLINE, CONTROL, FEAR . . .
MRS. DAGGER, WHO ARE YOU TALKING TO?
MISS FLUNKE, I . . . ?!
IT'S TIME FOR MORNING ANNOUNCEMENTS, MA'AM.
YES, YES, OF COURSE.

A HOCKEY STICK? I SEND YOU OUT TO BRING ME STUFF. AND YOU COME BACK WITH A HOCKEY STICK?
WHAT DO I WANT WITH A HOCKEY STICK?
I'M HUNGRY.
ZING
DIDN'T ANY OF YOU MORONS BRING ME FOOD?
I DID, JOE!
WARTIE

LEMME SEE.
NOT BAD.
ACK!
UGG!
CHOKE!
BURP!
WHAT THE . . . BUBBLES?
WHERE'D YA GET THIS?
I TOOK IT FROM THIS DWEEB NAMED WARTIE.
FIND HIM! NOBODY MESSES WITH JOE ROMAN. I'LL SHOW WARTIE WHO RULES THE SCHOOL.
WARTIE
WARTIE

WHAT DO YOU MEAN WHOEVER OPENS THAT LOCKER RULES THE SCHOOL?
001 XCL
IT'S AN OLD SCHOOL LEGEND.
WHY IS IT BY ITSELF?
DUNNO. CREEPY, HUH?
WHAT'S THAT?
001 XCL
IF YOUR HEART BE TRUE AND FINE, TURN THE DIAL LEFT TO 9.
27 TO THE RIGHT, GIVES THE OWNER STRENGTH AND MIGHT.
LEFT AGAIN TO NUMBER 3, A KING TO ALL THE STUDENTS BE.
IT'S THE COMBINATION. BUT NOBODY CAN MAKE IT WORK.

EVERY YEAR, SOME KIDS TRY TO OPEN THAT BEAT-UP OLD THING.
THEY SAY THAT IF YOU OPEN IT, YOU'LL GET EVERYTHING YOU WANT.
SOME KIDS SWEAR THEY'VE HEARD *TAPPING* FROM INSIDE, LIKE IT'S *HAUNTED* OR THERE'S SOMEBODY *TRAPPED* IN THERE. PERSONALLY, I DON'T BELIEVE THAT STUFF. I THINK THAT LOCKER IS JUST RUSTED SHUT.
IF YOUR HEART BE TRUE AND FINE, TURN THE DIAL LEFT TO 9.
27 TO THE RIGHT, GIVES THE OWNER STRENGTH AND MIGHT.
LEFT AGAIN TO NUMBER 3, A KING TO ALL THE STUDENTS BE.
OH, REALLY?
HEY, ARTIE!
WE BETTER GET GOING.
WHAT'S WRONG?
IT'S FERRYMAN. I DON'T THINK YOUR LUNCH AGREED WITH HIM.
THAT'S HIM, THAT'S THE KID!

WHAT DID YOUR SISTER PUT IN THAT SANDWICH?
OOOF!
OH, NO, HANNIBAL!

HANNIBAL?
CRUNCH
YOU LITTLE RUNT. YOU TRIED TO *POISON* ME.
SSSSORRY. I WAS . . .
YOU'LL BE SORRY ALRIGHT. . .

NOBODY MESSES WITH . . .
JOSEPH ROMAN, WHAT'S GOING ON HERE?
HULLO, MRS. DAGGER.
I'M SURPRISED AT YOU, YOUNG MAN.
SORRY, MRS. DAGGER.
YOU SHOULD KNOW BETTER.
WHY AREN'T YOU BOYS PRACTICING DODGEBALL?

HANNIBAL?
I WANT YOU TO WIN THE DISTRICT TROPHY AGAIN.
I HAVE A VERY GOOD FEELING ABOUT THIS SEASON.
NO LONGER SHALL WE CRAWL IN THE LOWER DIVISIONS.
NO SIR, THIS TIME, *VICTORY* IS WITHIN OUR GRASP.
THIS YEAR THE MIGHTY WILL FALL . . .
YOU! IN MY OFFICE. *NOW!*

WHAT ARE YOU IN FOR?
UM, IT'S HARD TO EXPLAIN. YOU?
PRINCIPAL'S OFFICE
GRAND THEFT GAME BOY.
YOU STOLE A GAME BOY?
PIZZA PLACE
NOT ME, YOU.
WHAT? I DID NOT!
RELAX. IT'S NOT STEALING. SORT OF, KIND OF, NOT REALLY.
THE GAME BOY IS MINE. WELL, REALLY IT'S MY BROTHER'S.
DAGGER TOOK IT. SEE? IT'S ON HER DESK.

YOU WANT ME TO STEAL IT??
SSHHHH! IT'S NOT STEALING! IT'S MORE LIKE RETRIEVING.
WHEN YOU GET IN THERE, I'LL GIVE YOU THE SIGNAL. JUST GRAB IT.
WHAT SIGNAL?
I KNEW I COULD COUNT ON YOU. LATER!
UH! WAIT! WHERE ARE YOU GOING?
WHERE IS WHO GOING?

AND WHO ARE YOU!? WHAT EDUCATIONAL BLACK HOLE SPIT YOU OUT AND BLESSED US WITH YOUR WORMLIKE PRESENCE?
MY NAME IS ARTHUR KING. I JUST MOVED FROM CORNWALL. I'M NEW.
YEAH. HOORAH. WONDERFUL. WE CERTAINLY ARE LUCKY HERE. LET'S SEE WHAT YOUR FILE SAYS.
HMMF, I SEE, YOU MUST BE SOOOO PROUD OF YOURSELF. B-MINUS. B-MINUS. C-PLUS. TELL ME, MR. KING, ARE YOU GOOD AT ANYTHING?
WELL, I'M . . .
THAT'S NOT A QUESTION. SIGH
1ST
I DON'T KNOW HOW THEY DO THINGS OVER IN CORNWALL, BUT AT CAMELOT MIDDLE SCHOOL, WE OPERATE ON ONLY THE HIGHEST OF STANDARDS.
1ST
WE DO NOT TOLERATE CONNIVING LITTLE WORMS THAT GO AROUND SUBVERTING THE EDUCATIONAL PROGRAM AND ASSAULTING OUR FACULTY.
I'M SORRY, BUT IT WAS AN ACCIDENT.

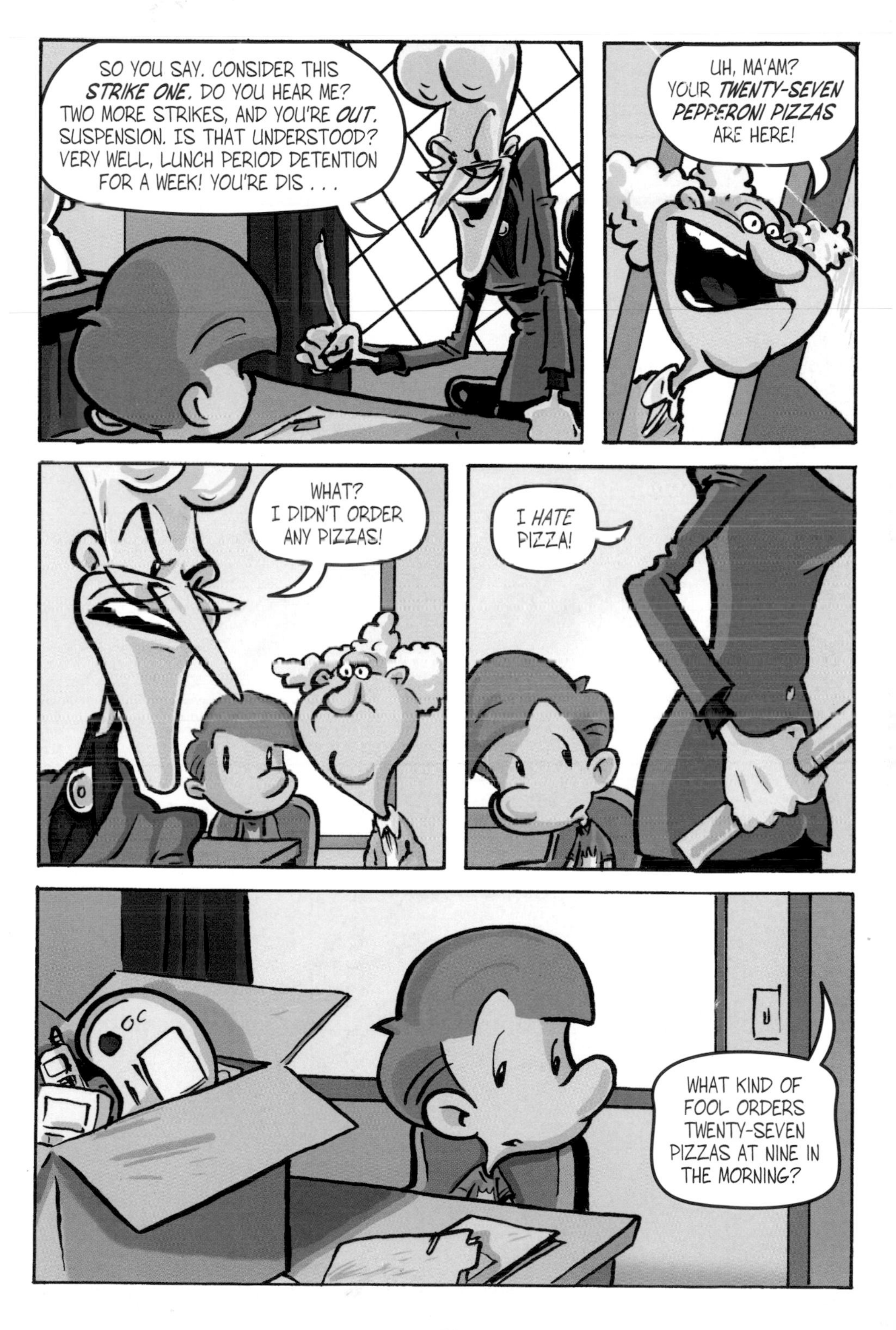
SO YOU SAY. CONSIDER THIS STRIKE ONE. DO YOU HEAR ME? TWO MORE STRIKES, AND YOU'RE OUT. SUSPENSION. IS THAT UNDERSTOOD? VERY WELL, LUNCH PERIOD DETENTION FOR A WEEK! YOU'RE DIS . . .
UH, MA'AM? YOUR TWENTY-SEVEN PEPPERONI PIZZAS ARE HERE!
WHAT? I DIDN'T ORDER ANY PIZZAS!
I HATE PIZZA!
WHAT KIND OF FOOL ORDERS TWENTY-SEVEN PIZZAS AT NINE IN THE MORNING?

PIZZA
PALACE

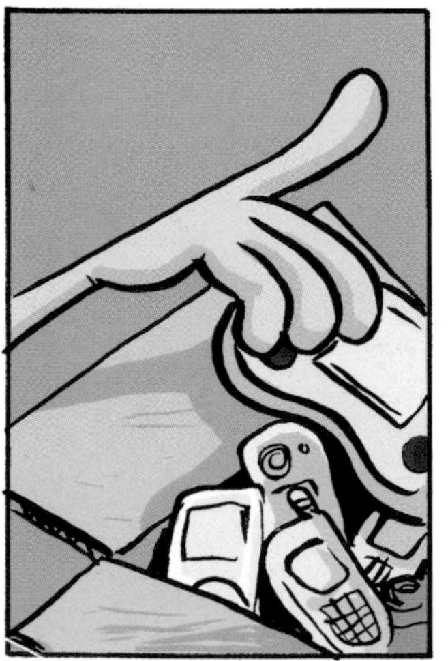

WHAT ARE YOU STILL DOING HERE?

UH, I DON'T HAVE A LOCKER YET, MA'AM.

A LOCKER, YOU SAY? MISS FLUNKE, WE MUST GIVE THIS FINE BOY A LOCKER!
MMM, THIS IS REALLY GOOD PIZZA. YOU SHOULD . . .
MISS FLUNKE, GIVE MR. KING LOCKER #001XCL.
YES, MA'AM, UH, THAT LOCKER IS . . .
IT HASN'T BEEN OPENED IN YEARS.
DON'T BE SILLY. GIVE MR. KING LOCKER #001XCL.
BUT . . .
GLADYS . . . GIVE . . . HIM . . . THE . . . LOCKER!
YES, MA'AM.
I WILL BE KEEPING AN EYE ON YOU, WORM. I KNOW WHAT YOU'RE UP TO. TWO MORE STRIKES, AND YOU'RE OUT. TWO MORE.

THIS SCHOOL IS BIGGER THAN IT LOOKS.
#001XCL, WHY DOES THAT SOUND FAMILIAR?
IS THAT THE ONE THAT DOESN'T OPEN?
LOCKER #001XCL
TAC TAC TAC
HANNIBAL, COME BACK!

WHERE'S HE
GOING?

I GOT
YOU NOW!

TOMATO SOUP
BANANAS BUNCH
WHO APPROACHES THE LADIES' LUNCH?
MY NAME IS ARTIE, I THINK I'M LOST.
BEANS OF GREEN
STICKS OF FISH
TELL US, CHILD. WHAT IS YOUR WISH?
WELL, I WAS LOOKING FOR MY LOCKER. IT'S #001XCL. BUT THEN I SAW . . .
HAM 'N CHEESE
AND ONIONS RING
'TIS THE LOCKER OF THE KING.
OK, HOW'D YOU KNOW MY LAST NAME?

CHICKEN PATTY
AND MACAROONS
BE FOREWARNED, A BATTLE LOOMS.
A BATTLE? WHAT?
CREAM OF CORN
BROCCOLI SPEARS
WHAT YOU SEEK IS WHAT HE FEARS.
WHO?
TRUE OF HEART A CHAMPION BE.
DRINK OF THIS,
THE SOUP OF PEA.
DID YOU SAY *PEE?* NO THANKS. I BETTER GO.

DUDE, DID YOU GET IT?
DID YOU SEE THOSE WEIRD. . .
HERE!
ALRIGHT! YOU ROCK! YOU RULE! YOU RIP! YOU RUN! YOU ROB! YOU . . . UH!
YEAH, RIGHT. BUT ABOUT THOSE . . .
THE NAME'S WAYNE.
ARTIE! YOU KNOW WAYNE?
KIND OF.
YOU KIDDING? HE'S MY NEW BEST FRIEND!
DID YOU GET A LOCKER?
YEAH . . . IT'S NUMBER. . . OH, OH, ONE. . . X. . . C. . . L.
NO WAY! HOW'D YOU GET THAT?
MRS. DAGGER GAVE IT TO ME.
DUDE, SHE MUST REALLY HATE YOU.

I DON'T . . . ?
THAT'S THE BUSTED LOCKER I SHOWED YOU THAT NOBODY CAN OPEN. THE ONE WITH THE RHYMING GRAFFITI ON IT.
I HEARD IT'S CURSED. THIS KID, TERRY WHITE, HAD THAT LOCKER. HE TRIED TO OPEN IT. AND THAT WAS THE LAST ANYBODY EVER SAW HIM. I THINK IT'S A DIMENSIONAL PORTAL TO A BARREN WASTELAND.
TERRY MOVED TO NEW JERSEY.
WHATEVER.
THIS IS TOO COOL! WAIT TILL EVERYONE FINDS OUT!
NO, DON'T! IT'S JUST A STUPID LOCKER.
BUT IF YOU OPEN IT, YOU'LL RULE THE SCHOOL.
JOIN FUTURE LEADERS
OST
AND IF I CAN'T?
THEN YOU'LL CARRY YOUR BOOKS AROUND ALL YEAR.
WHAT'S YOUR NEXT CLASS?
SCIENCE WITH . . .

MR. MERLYN, HE'S LATE. RAAWK!
WHAT? OH, SORRY, IT'S YOU!
PAY NO ATTENTION TO OBERON. WHAT HE'S TRYING TO SAY IS . . .
QUIZ
ARTHUR KING OF CORNWALL. WE'VE BEEN EXPECTING YOU.
YOU HAVE? HOW DID YOU KNOW?
THERE IS MUCH THAT IS KNOWN TO ME. I KNOW WHY THE SUN SETS. I KNOW WHY THE MOON RISES. I KNOW WHY THE LEAVES CHANGE IN AUTUMN.
I WAS TOLD OF THE ARRIVAL OF A KING.
REALLY, BY WHO?

THE MAIN OFFICE. I'M ALSO YOUR FACULTY ADVISOR. WHAT TOOK YOU SO LONG?
I GOT LOST. THERE WERE THESE THREE . . .
OH, YOU MET THE LADIES OF THE LUNCH.
YEAH, THEY'RE KIND OF . . .
WEIRD? RIGHT. HAIRNETS ARE TOO TIGHT, IF YOU ASK ME. THEY SAY THEY SEE THE FUTURE BY READING THE LUNCH MENU.
LIKE TODAY FOR INSTANCE: CHICKEN PATTY AND MACAROONS.
LUNCH
BE FOREWARNED, A BATTLE LOOMS.
REALLY? I'M GLAD I BROUGHT MY LUNCH. NOW WHERE WAS I?
RAAWK! POP QUIZ!
THANK YOU, OBERON.
QUIZ
I DID TELL YOU YOU'D BE TESTED.

DANGER! RAAWK!
KNOCK, KNOCK
MR. MERLYN.
IS THIS A DAGGER I SEE BEFORE ME?
MAY I SPEAK TO YOU FOR A MOMENT? IN PRIVATE.
YES, OF COURSE. BUT, I WANT YOU TO KNOW I HAD NO IDEA ABOUT THE PIZZAS.
MR. MERLYN, YOU'VE BEEN HERE EIGHT YEARS.
NINE, I'VE BEEN HERE NINE YEARS.
WHATEVER. WHAT I'M TRYING TO SAY IS, DON'T YOU THINK A MAN OF YOUR UNIQUE ABILITIES WOULD BE MUCH BETTER SERVED AT ANOTHER SCHOOL? A SCHOOL FAR, FAR AWAY. IN ANOTHER DISTRICT.
I GET YOUR POINT. YOU WANT TO GET RID OF ME.
NO.
YES.

DON'T BE A FOOL, MERLYN. IT'S NOT THAT WE DON'T GET ALONG, BUT RIGHT NOW I RULE CAMELOT. THINK OF YOUR FUTURE . . .
I AM.
ROOM 9
MY FUTURE IS TIED TO THEIR FUTURE. AND I'M STAYING HERE. SORRY TO DISAPPOINT YOU.
HMMF. BY THE WAY, YOU'VE BEEN ASSIGNED LUNCH DETENTION THIS WEEK.
AGAIN?
THE MENU WAS RIGHT.
A BATTLE DOES LOOM!
LUNCH

HEY, ARTIE! WAIT UP!
WHAT'S GOING ON?
I'M GOING TO TRY TO OPEN MY LOCKER.
WHO CARES IF I CAN'T OPEN IT? IT'S NOT LIKE ANYBODY WILL FIND OUT.
THERE HE IS!
THAT'S THE NEW KID!
IF YOUR HEART BE TRUE AND FINE, TURN THE DIAL LEFT TO 9.
27 TO THE RIGHT, GIVES THE OWNER STRENGTH AND MIGHT.
LEFT AGAIN TO NUMBER 3, A KING TO ALL THE STUDENTS BE.
OPEN IT!
HOW DID *THEY* FIND OUT?

HEY, GUYS!
DID YOU TELL EVERYBODY?
NOOO. NOT EVERYBODY. JUST A COUPLE KIDS IN THE LIBRARY, A FEW IN GYM CLASS AND A HANDFUL IN STUDY HALL.
OPEN IT!
YEAH!
WE WANNA SEE THE SKELETON!
WHAT DO I DO?
TRY TO OPEN IT. IT'S YOUR LOCKER.
IF YOUR HEART BE TRUE AND FINE, TURN THE DIAL LEFT TO 9.
27 TO THE RIGHT, GIVES THE OWNER STRENGTH AND MIGHT.
LEFT AGAIN TO NUMBER 3, A KING TO ALL THE STUDENTS BE.
OK.
DON'T TOUCH THAT LOCKER!

IF ANYONE IS GOING TO OPEN THIS LOCKER, IT'S GONNA BE ME!
OUTTA THE WAY, SQUIRT!
IF YOUR HEART BE TRUE AND FINE, TURN THE DIAL LEFT TO 9.
27 TO THE RIGHT, GIVES THE OWNER STRENGTH AND MIGHT.
LEFT AGAIN TO NUMBER 3, A KING TO ALL THE STUDENTS BE.
NOTHING TO IT! 9-27-3.
IF YOUR HEART BE TRUE AND FINE, TURN THE DIAL LEFT TO 9.
27 TO THE RIGHT, GIVES THE OWNER STRENGTH AND MIGHT.
LEFT AGAIN TO NUMBER 3, A KING TO ALL THE STUDENTS BE.
MUST BE STUCK!

UUHH
GRUNT
PANT
BAM
HUFF, PUFF, IT CAN'T . . .
HUFF, BE OPENED, PUFF.
LET THE NEW KID TRY!

IF I CAN'T DO IT, NOBODY CAN. BUT BE MY GUEST, *WIMP.*
STRENGTH AND MIGHT.
LEFT AGAIN TO NUMBER 3, A KING TO ALL THE STUDENTS BE.
WAIT . . . WHAT IF IT *IS* A GATEWAY TO ANOTHER DIMENSION?
IF YOUR HEART BE TRUE AND FINE, TURN THE DIAL LEFT TO 9.
27 TO THE RIGHT, GIVES THE OWNER STRENGTH AND MIGHT.
MAYBE IT'S LIKE THAT MOVIE AND YOU'RE THE *CHOSEN ONE!*
OR MAYBE . . .
IT'S JUST A BUSTED LOCKER.

IF YOUR HEART BE TRUE AND FINE,
TURN THE DIAL LEFT TO NINE.
TWENTY-SEVEN TO THE RIGHT,
001 XCL
GIVES THE OWNER STRENGTH AND MIGHT.
LEFT AGAIN TO NUMBER THREE,
A KING TO ALL THE STUDENTS BE.

CLICK
AAAAHHHH
YEAH! HE DID IT!
OOOOOOHHHHHHHH
THERE'S NOTHING IN IT.
IT'S EMPTY.
HE STILL OPENED IT.
ARTIE RULES THE SCHOOL!
ARTIE ART

SHUDDUP!

IF ANYONE THINKS THEY CAN BEAT ME, STEP RIGHT UP!
AS FOR YOU, YOU THINK YOU'RE FUNNY? THINK YOU CAN MAKE ME LOOK STUPID? I'M GONNA BOUNCE YOU LIKE A DODGEBALL.
NOBODY MESSES WITH JOE ROMAN.
WAIT! LET HIM GO! LET'S SETTLE THIS A DIFFERENT WAY. HOW ABOUT DODGEBALL? OUR TEAM AGAINST THE HORDE.

HUH? WE'LL KILL YOU. WE'RE *UNDEFEATED.*
OK, BUT IF WE WIN, YOU HAVE TO LEAVE US ALONE.
AND WHEN *WE* WIN, HE SHOWS ME HOW TO OPEN THIS LOCKER, AND I PROVE ONCE AND FOR ALL THAT *I* RULE THIS SCHOOL.
27 TO THE
GIVES THE OWNER
STRENGTH
AND MIGHT
DEAL.
YOU HEARD THE GEEK! ***DODGEBALL MATCH,*** FRIDAY AFTER SCHOOL, ***GEEKS*** AGAINST ***THE HORDE,*** WINNERS RULE THE SCHOOL!

WHAT DID YOU DO THAT FOR?
I SAVED YOUR LIFE. BESIDES, YOU'RE A DODGEBALL LEGEND, RIGHT? YOU WERE ALL-STATE, FIRST TEAM.
YOU WERE ALL-STATE? IS THAT GOOD?
FINALLY, WE'RE GONNA GET EVEN WITH THE HORDE!
LISTEN, ACTUALLY I WAS . . .
DUDE, I'M STARVING.
WE'LL HAVE TIME TO DISCUSS THIS AT LUNCH.
LUNCH, THAT'S RIGHT, I DON'T HAVE ONE.
WHAT'S THIS?
WHERE'D THIS COME FROM?

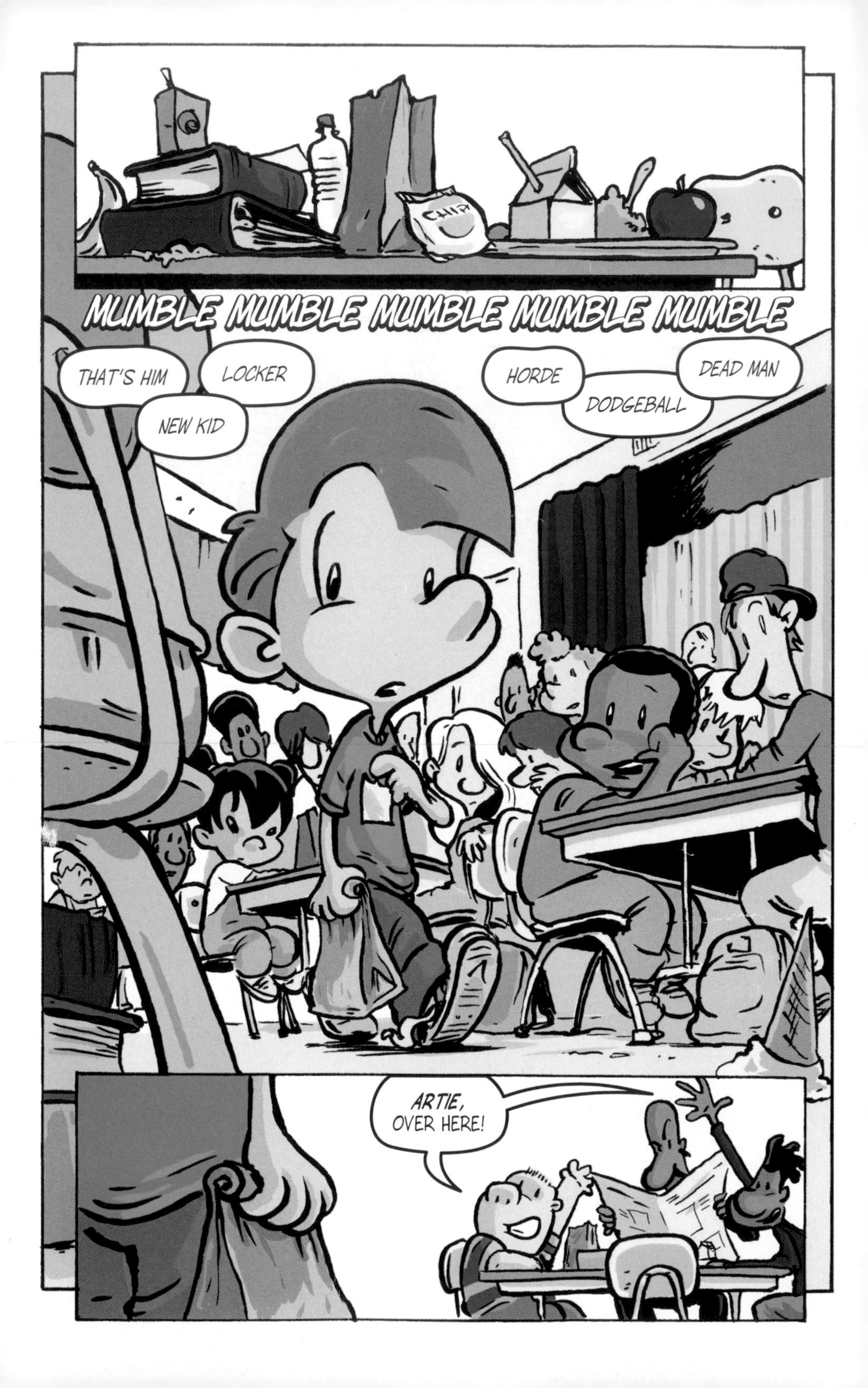
CHIPS
MUMBLE MUMBLE MUMBLE MUMBLE MUMBLE
THAT'S HIM
NEW KID
LOCKER
HORDE
DODGEBALL
DEAD MAN
ARTIE, OVER HERE!

GREETINGS, ARTHUR OF CORNWALL. YOU HAVE MADE QUITE A NAME FOR YOURSELF.
WELL . . .
DUDE! *YOU RULE!* EVERYBODY IS TALKING ABOUT YOU!
WHERE DID YOU GET THE LUNCH?
I FOUND IT IN THE LOCKER.
ANY GOOD?
YEAH, BALONEY ON WHITE. NO CRUST, NO MUSTARD.
THE *LOCKER* CUTS OFF YOUR *CRUST?* TRADE YA!
LOOK, I DON'T WANT TO DO THIS.
FINE. IT'S ONLY A BALONEY SANDWICH.

NO, I MEAN THE DODGEBALL GAME.
PIZZ
ARTIE, FOR YEARS THE HORDE HAS BEEN PUSHING US AROUND. THEN YOU SHOW UP AND EVERYTHING CHANGES. WE'VE BEEN WAITING FOR SOMEONE LIKE YOU. WE CAN BEAT THEM. I KNOW IT.
BUT I'M JUST . . .
YOU'RE LIKE THAT CHOSEN ONE GUY. YOU MADE JOE EAT SOAP, YOU TRIPPED DAGGER, YOU GOT MY GAME BOY BACK AND YOU OPENED THE CURSED LOCKER.
YOU, MY FRIEND, ARE THE CHOSEN ONE, THE LEGEND.
PALACE
I'M NOT THE CHOSEN ONE! I'M USUALLY THE LAST CHOSEN ONE!
WHAT DO YOU THINK, MR. MERLYN?
SPORTS
WIZARDS BEAT CAVS

THERE COMES A TIME WHEN LIKE-MINDED FELLOWS GATHER TOGETHER TO CHART THEIR DESTINY.
SOME CALL IT FATE. OTHERS CALL IT LUCK.
ALL I KNOW IS THAT YOU THREE WERE SENT HERE FOR A REASON.
REALLY?
I KNEW IT!
AND THAT IS?
DETENTION! NOW, BE QUIET AND EAT.
PIZZA

THE NEXT MORNING
SORRY I HAD TO WORK LATE, KIDS. HOW WAS YOUR FIRST DAY?
GREAT, MOM! I'VE ALREADY GOT CHEERLEADING TRYOUTS TODAY.
THAT'S TERRIFIC, MORGAN. WHAT ABOUT YOU, ARTIE?
I DON'T LIKE CHEERLEADING.
HA HA VERY FUNNY, YOU KNOW WHAT I MEANT.
ARTIE'S PLAYING IN A BIG DODGEBALL GAME ON FRIDAY!
IS THIS TRUE? THIS FRIDAY? I'LL BE THERE.
I'M SOOO PROUD OF YOU. JUMPING RIGHT BACK ON THE HORSE.

I'LL SEE YOU TONIGHT. GOOD LUCK WITH THE TRYOUTS, MORGAN.
THANKS, MOM. BYE-BYE.
WARTIE, WHAT ARE YOU DOING?
Valiant Flakes
TRYING TO EAT MY CEREAL.
NO, I MEAN TELLING EVERYONE YOU'RE A DODGEBALL STAR. AS IF!
I BETTER GET MY DIARY BACK BECAUSE IF I DON'T?
MORGAN
I'M GONNA TELL ALL YOUR LITTLE FRIENDS THAT YOU'RE REALLY A DODGEBALL LOSER.
MORGAN

UH . . . WHAT'S THIS?
MISSING TARANTULA
SWEET! YOU MADE POSTERS? THANKS!
I DIDN'T MAKE THEM. I FOUND THEM, IN THE LOCKER.
THIS LOCKER? THE MAGIC SANDWICH LOCKER?
UH-HUH.
YEAH, RIGHT.

ANYWAYS, WAYNE AND I THINK IT WOULD BE A GOOD IDEA IF WE HAD A DODGEBALL PRACTICE.
PRACTICE!?
AND FINE, TURN THE DIAL LEFT TO 9.
27 TO THE RIGHT, GIVES THE OWNER STRENGTH AND MIGHT.
LEFT AGAIN TO NUMBER 3, A KING TO ALL THE STUDENTS BE.
I KNOW, *YOU* DON'T NEED IT. BUT *WE* DO.
YEAH, BUT . . .
BESIDES, MAYBE YOU CAN TEACH US A FEW MOVES.
OK, BUT . . .
COOL! I'LL TELL WAYNE! THANKS AGAIN FOR THE POSTERS. I'LL GO HANG THEM UP!
AW, FISH STICKS, I'M *DOOMED.*
ARE YOU OK?

HI, MY NAME IS GWEN LEE.
I'M ARTIE KING.
I KNOW. YOU'RE THE LOCKER KID, KING OF CAMELOT MIDDLE SCHOOL, DODGEBALL LEGEND, ALL-STATE, FIRST TEAM.
YEAH, WELL, IT WAS A SMALL STATE . . .
I'M GLAD YOU'RE TAKING ON THE HORDE. I HOPE YOU CREAM THEM. THEY DESTROYED MY VILLAGE.
REALLY?
IT WASN'T A REAL VILLAGE, JUST A PROJECT I DID FOR SOCIAL STUDIES.
OH?
SO, WHAT'S YOUR TEAM CALLED?
WE HAVEN'T GOT A NAME.

WHAT? EVERY TEAM NEEDS A NAME. SOMETHING COOL LIKE THE KNIGHTS.
NIGHTS?
AS IN . . . DAYS AND NIGHTS?
AS IN . . . KNIGHTS OF THE VALIANT BLADE.
YOU LIKE THE VALIANT BLADE? ME, TOO!
WHATCHA GOT THERE?
UH, OH, POSTERS TO FIND A MISSING HANNIBAL. I MEAN A SPIDER.
MISSING
CAN I HANG SOME FOR YOU?
YEAH, SURE, THANKS!
SEE YA AROUND.

RAWWK!
HAIL TO THE KING!
MR. MERLYN?
WHAT CAN I DO FOR YOU, ARTHUR?
YOU KNOW I HAVE THIS LOCKER?
YES I KNOW. #001XCL. IT HASN'T BEEN OPENED IN YEARS. THAT'S QUITE A CROWNING ACHIEVEMENT.
THAT'S WHAT I HEAR. ANYWAYS, I'VE BEEN FINDING STUFF IN IT. STUFF THAT WASN'T THERE BEFORE.
WHAT KIND OF STUFF? SKELETONS? STACKS OF MONEY? DIMENSIONAL PORTALS?

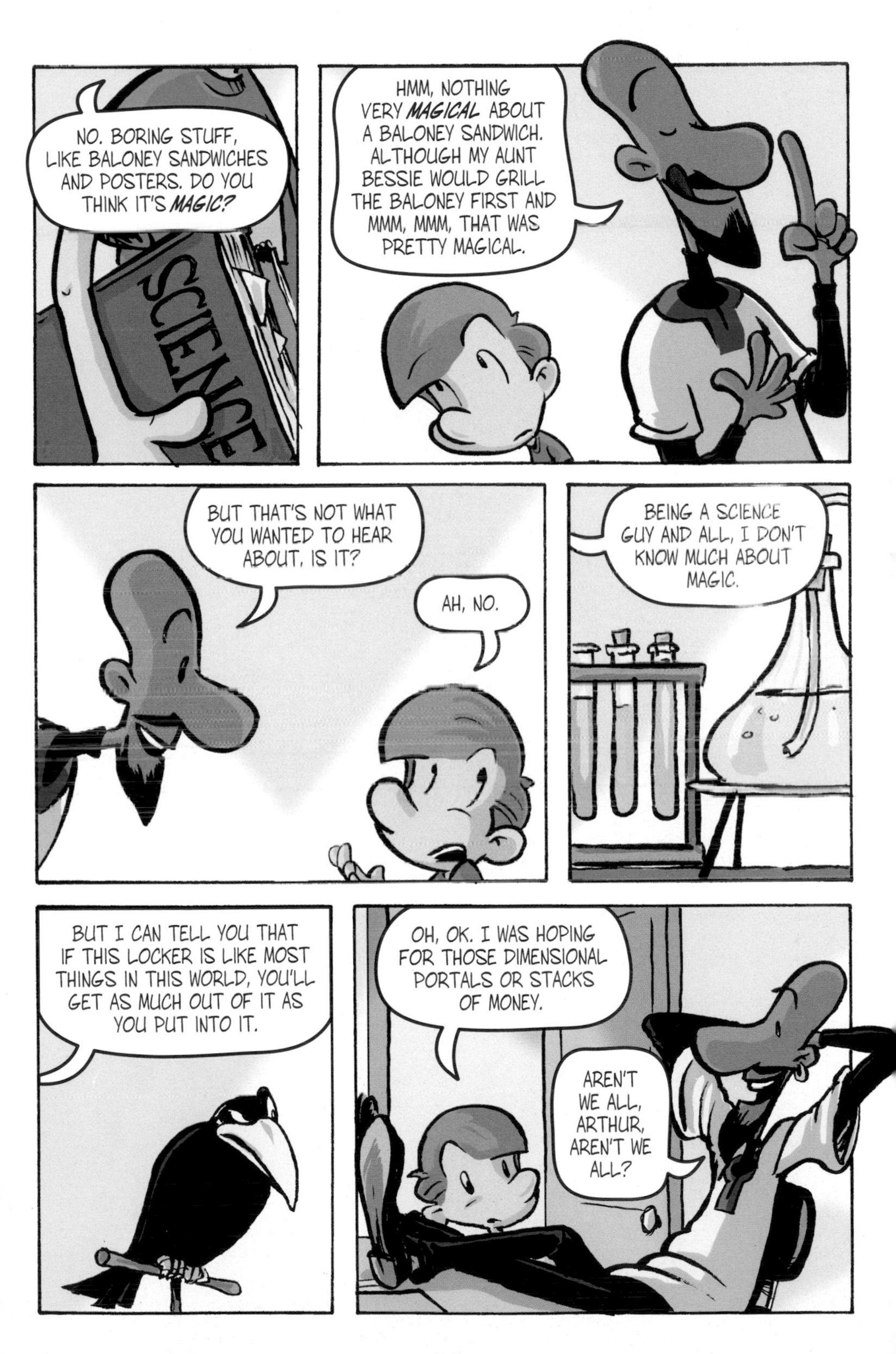
NO. BORING STUFF, LIKE BALONEY SANDWICHES AND POSTERS. DO YOU THINK IT'S MAGIC?
SCIENCE
HMM, NOTHING VERY MAGICAL ABOUT A BALONEY SANDWICH. ALTHOUGH MY AUNT BESSIE WOULD GRILL THE BALONEY FIRST AND MMM, MMM, THAT WAS PRETTY MAGICAL.
BUT THAT'S NOT WHAT YOU WANTED TO HEAR ABOUT, IS IT?
AH, NO.
BEING A SCIENCE GUY AND ALL, I DON'T KNOW MUCH ABOUT MAGIC.
BUT I CAN TELL YOU THAT IF THIS LOCKER IS LIKE MOST THINGS IN THIS WORLD, YOU'LL GET AS MUCH OUT OF IT AS YOU PUT INTO IT.
OH, OK. I WAS HOPING FOR THOSE DIMENSIONAL PORTALS OR STACKS OF MONEY.
AREN'T WE ALL, ARTHUR, AREN'T WE ALL?

MISSING
TARANTULA
ARTHUR KING
LOCKER # 001XCL
WHEN I FIND THAT *LITTLE RUNT*, I'LL SMASH HIM.

OH, NO!
SOMEONE TORE DOWN ALL THE POSTERS!
WHAT JERK WOULD DO THAT?
HEY, *WIMP*.
YOU THINK YOU CAN *SCARE* ME?
GOING AROUND TELLING EVERYONE YOU'RE ALL-STATE, FIRST-TEAM, DODGEBALL KING OF CORNWALL? YOU THINK YOU CAN *BEAT* ME?
JOE, I . . .

SHUDDUP! I'VE HAD ENOUGH OF YOU. I'M GONNA . . . SP. . . SP. . . SPIDER???
HANNIBAL?
SLAM
NEXT TIME, LOSER, I'M GONNA PUT YOU IN THIS LOCKER AND SLAM IT SHUT!

WHEW!

HANNIBAL?!

WAIT UNTIL PERCY FINDS OUT.

HE'S GONE!

THE ONLY ONE WHO IS GONE IS YOU, MR. KING.

YOU KNOW WHAT THIS IS?

THIS IS STRIKE TWO. DO YOU HEAR ME? STRIKE TWO!

NOW PICK THIS MESS UP.

I'LL BE WATCHING YOU.

AFTER SCHOOL
SO, WHERE IS HE?
HE SAID HE'D BE HERE. HE'LL BE HERE.
SORRY, I'M LATE. MRS. DAGGER MADE ME CLEAN UP ALL THOSE RIPPED POSTERS.
I THINK I SAW HANNIBAL.
WHAT? WHERE?
HE WAS IN MY LOCKER. BUT WHEN I LOOKED AGAIN HE WAS GONE.
TOLD YOU, DIMENSIONAL PORTAL.
YOU KNOW THAT GIRL GWEN?
GWENDOLYN LEE? WHY, YOU LIKE HER?
NO! SHE SAYS OUR TEAM NEEDS A NAME.
THAT'S NOT A BAD IDEA.
YEAH! HOW ABOUT THE DECAPITATORS!

THE *SKULL CRUSHERS* OF CAMELOT!
THE *PRINCIPAL IMPALERS!*
THE *HORDE SMASHERS!*
THE *DAGGER SMACKERS!*
ACTUALLY, SHE SUGGESTED *"KNIGHTS."*
NIGHTS? LIKE, NIGHTS OF THE LIVING DEAD!
KNIGHTS OF COLUMBUS?
NO, JUST *"KNIGHTS."*
THAT'S *LAME*. WE PRACTICING OR WHAT?
YEAH.

HOW SHOULD WE START?
YOU'VE GOT THE MOST EXPERIENCE, SHOW US YOUR STUFF.
YEAH, BUT NO RUNNING LAPS. I HATE RUNNING LAPS.
UM, OK, THIS IS A DODGEBALL. AND THE MOST IMPORTANT THING TO REMEMBER IS NOT TO GET HIT WITH THE DODGEBALL.
HEH-HEH, JUST KIDDING.
CAN'T YOU SHOW US SOMETHING WE DON'T KNOW? LIKE DODGING. CAN YOU TEACH US DODGING?
DODGING?
YEAH. SHOW US. GIMME THAT BALL AND WE'LL TRY AND HIT YOU.

OK, SURE, I GUESS.
THERE ARE THREE THINGS TO REMEMBER.
THE FIRST THING IS TO BE PREPARED.
OH, LOOK. MY SHOE'S UNTIED.
THE SECOND IS TO KEEP YOUR EYE ON THE BALL.
THE THIRD IS . . . DAAAAAHDDGG!
POW

ARTIE, ARE YOU OK?
DUDE, YOU STINK.
HE WAS TYING HIS SHOE.
SORRY. HOW WAS I TO KNOW IT WASN'T SOME KIND OF NINJA DODGEBALL STANCE?
WHAT ARE YOU GUYS DOING?
OH, HEY, GWEN. THIS IS OUR TEAM PRACTICE.
COOL. IS THIS YOUR WHOLE TEAM? WHERE'S YOUR FOURTH PLAYER? DODGEBALL REQUIRES THAT YOU HAVE AT LEAST FOUR PLAYERS ON A TEAM.

UH, WE DON'T HAVE A FOURTH.
CAN I BE IT? I PLAY DODGEBALL WITH MY OLDER BROTHERS ALL THE TIME. I'M PRETTY GOOD.
GEE, THANKS, THAT SOUNDS . . .
TERRIBLE! SHE'S A GIRL! GIRLS CAN'T PLAY!
AND YOU'RE A JERK. ACTUALLY, YOU'RE ALL JERKS! I TAKE BACK WHAT I SAID, YOU GUYS AREN'T THE KNIGHTS, YOU'RE THE DOPES. I HOPE YOU GET CREAMED.
WHAT???

SHE'S A GIRL. IT'S A KNOWN FACT, GIRLS CAN'T PLAY DODGEBALL.
AND YET YOU'RE A MORON, BUT WE LET YOU PLAY.
GWEN HAS A POINT. WE NEED A FOURTH.
NO PROBLEM, I GOT AN IDEA!
THIS CAN'T BE GOOD.
IN A VIDEO GAME, WHEN YOU'RE STUCK, WHAT DO YOU DO?
GET THE CHEAT CODE?
THIS IS TRUE. BUT WHAT IF YOU CAN'T FIND THE CHEAT CODE? YOU HIRE A MERCENARY.
A DODGEBALL MERCENARY?
HERE WE GO.
YOU KNOW ONE?
YES, WE GET SCOTT SAVAGE. MY BROTHER IS FRIENDS WITH HIM.

THAT'S THE LAMEST IDEA EVER!
I DON'T HEAR YOU COMING UP WITH A BETTER ONE, "MR. LET'S-CHALLENGE-THE-HORDE-TO-DODGEBALL."
WHO'S SCOTT SAVAGE?
HE'S THE TOUGHEST KID IN TOWN! I HEARD THAT EVEN JOE IS AFRAID OF HIM.
REALLY?
SCOTT IS A PSYCHO! I HEARD HE CARRIES A KNIFE.
I GOT A JACKKNIFE IN BOY SCOUTS.
HE DOES MORE THAN WHITTLE WITH HIS.
OH. MAYBE WE SHOULDN'T GET THIS GUY.
THINK ABOUT IT. GOT TO GO, I'M LATE FOR DINNER.
SOMETHING TELLS ME THIS IS A BAD IDEA.

THE NEXT DAY
WHAT'S THAT?
IT'S MY GAME BOY. I CAN'T DO STUDY HALL WITHOUT IT.
WHAT IF YOU GET CAUGHT AGAIN?
YOU GUYS ARE WORRYWARTS. NOTHING IS GOING TO . . .
HELLO, GENTLEMEN.
I SURE HOPE YOU HAVE YOUR HALL PASSES.
WHERE DO YOU THREE THINK YOU'RE GOING?
WE WERE JUST. . .
WHAT IS THAT?
UH . . .
I KNOW WHAT THAT IS. THAT IS STRIKE THREE. DO YOU KNOW WHAT THAT MEANS?

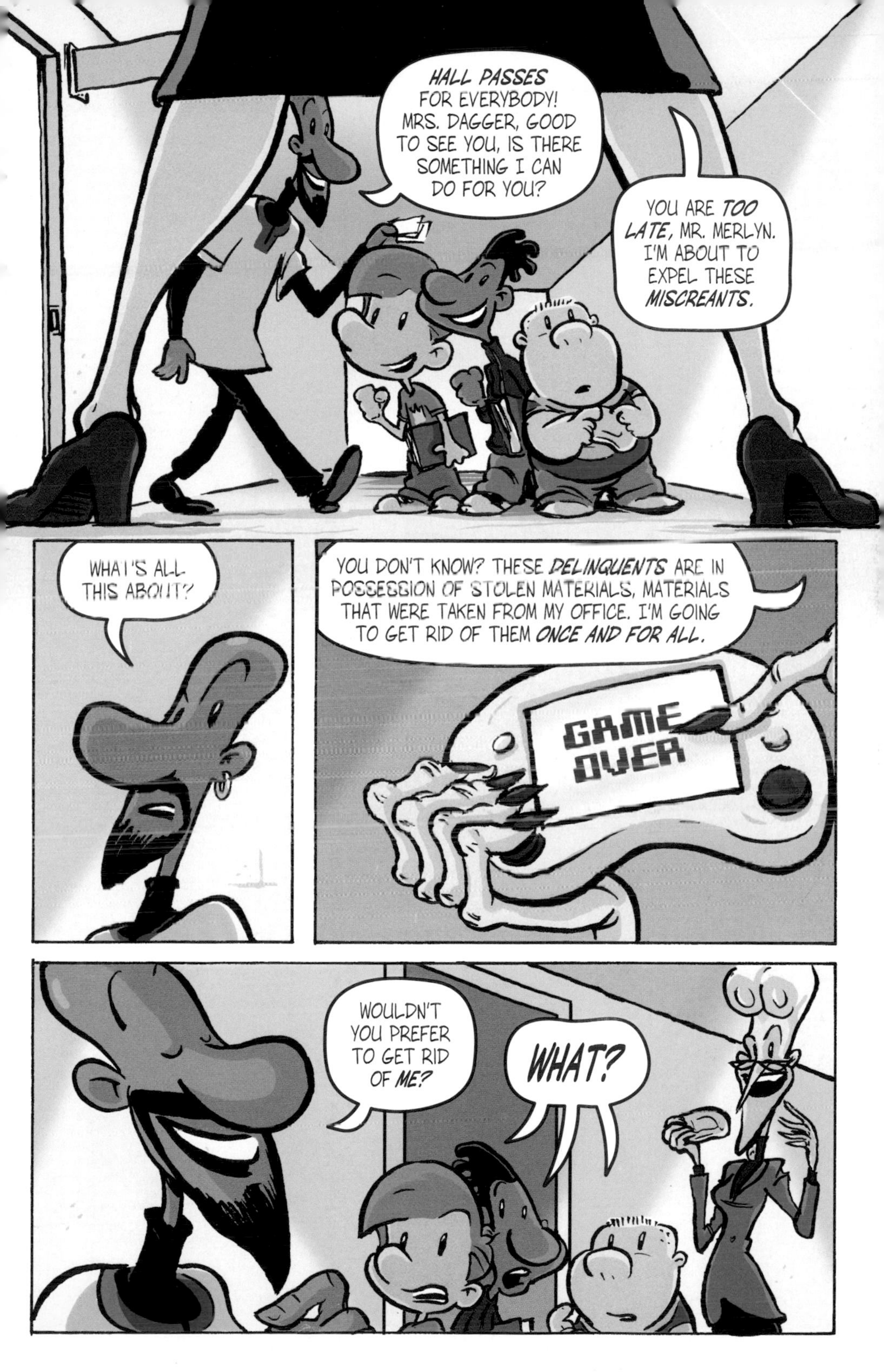
HALL PASSES FOR EVERYBODY! MRS. DAGGER, GOOD TO SEE YOU, IS THERE SOMETHING I CAN DO FOR YOU?
YOU ARE TOO LATE, MR. MERLYN. I'M ABOUT TO EXPEL THESE MISCREANTS.
WHAT'S ALL THIS ABOUT?
YOU DON'T KNOW? THESE DELINQUENTS ARE IN POSSESSION OF STOLEN MATERIALS, MATERIALS THAT WERE TAKEN FROM MY OFFICE. I'M GOING TO GET RID OF THEM ONCE AND FOR ALL.
GAME OVER
WOULDN'T YOU PREFER TO GET RID OF ME?
WHAT?

I'M NOT SURE I KNOW WHAT YOU ARE TALKING ABOUT, MR. MERLYN.
I'M TALKING ABOUT A LITTLE WAGER. ARE YOU AWARE OF A CERTAIN DODGEBALL GAME ON FRIDAY BETWEEN THESE BOYS AND ANOTHER GROUP, JOE'S HORDE?
DODGEBALL? YES, HMMM. YOU SAY THESE THREE AGAINST THE HORDE? PLEASE, TELL ME MORE.
IF THE HORDE WINS, INSTEAD OF THESE GUYS GETTING EXPELLED, I'LL QUIT.
REALLY? MY, MY, THAT IS TEMPTING. AND IF THEY SHOULD SOMEHOW WIN?
ARTHUR, WAYNE, PERCY AND I STAY, AND YOU MUST WEAR A GORILLA SUIT TO SCHOOL.
DEAL! I'LL HAVE THE EXIT PAPERS READY FOR YOU TO SIGN.
I'LL RENT THE GORILLA SUIT.

I DON'T THINK I'VE EVER SEEN HER SO HAPPY.
MR. MERLYN, THANKS, BUT WE DON'T WANT YOU TO QUIT.
NEITHER DO I. BUT I HAVE *FAITH* IN YOU, ARTHUR. BESIDES, THEY TELL ME YOU'RE A DODGEBALL LEGEND.
BUT THE HORDE *CHEATS!*
NOT THIS TIME! I'LL BE ONE OF *THE REFS.*
WHAT DO WE DO *NOW?*
WE GO GET SCOTT SAVAGE.
YEAH!

AFTER SCHOOL
IF YOUR HEART BE TRUE AND FINE, TURN THE DIAL
I HOPE THERE'S SOMETHING TO EAT IN HERE, I'M STARVING.
ALRIGHT!
GEE, THANKS.
DOGGY SNACKS
YOU READY?
I GUESS SO.
IF YOUR HEART BE TRUE AND FINE, TURN THE DIAL
SO, WHERE DO WE FIND THIS SCOTT KID?
A KING TO ALL THE STUDENTS BE.
DUDE, HE RULES ARCADIA.

THIS IS ARCADIA?
SCOTT SAVAGE HANGS OUT IN A MALL?
Welcome to HADRIAN'S MALL
ARCADIA IS AN ARCADE IN THE MALL. SCOTT'S UNCLE OWNS IT.
arcadia
I'M NOT ALLOWED TO GO TO THE MALL BY MYSELF.
YEAH, MY MOM THINKS I'M AT MATH CLUB.
DON'T WORRY. WE'LL BE IN AND OUT. THERE'LL BE NOTHING TO IT.

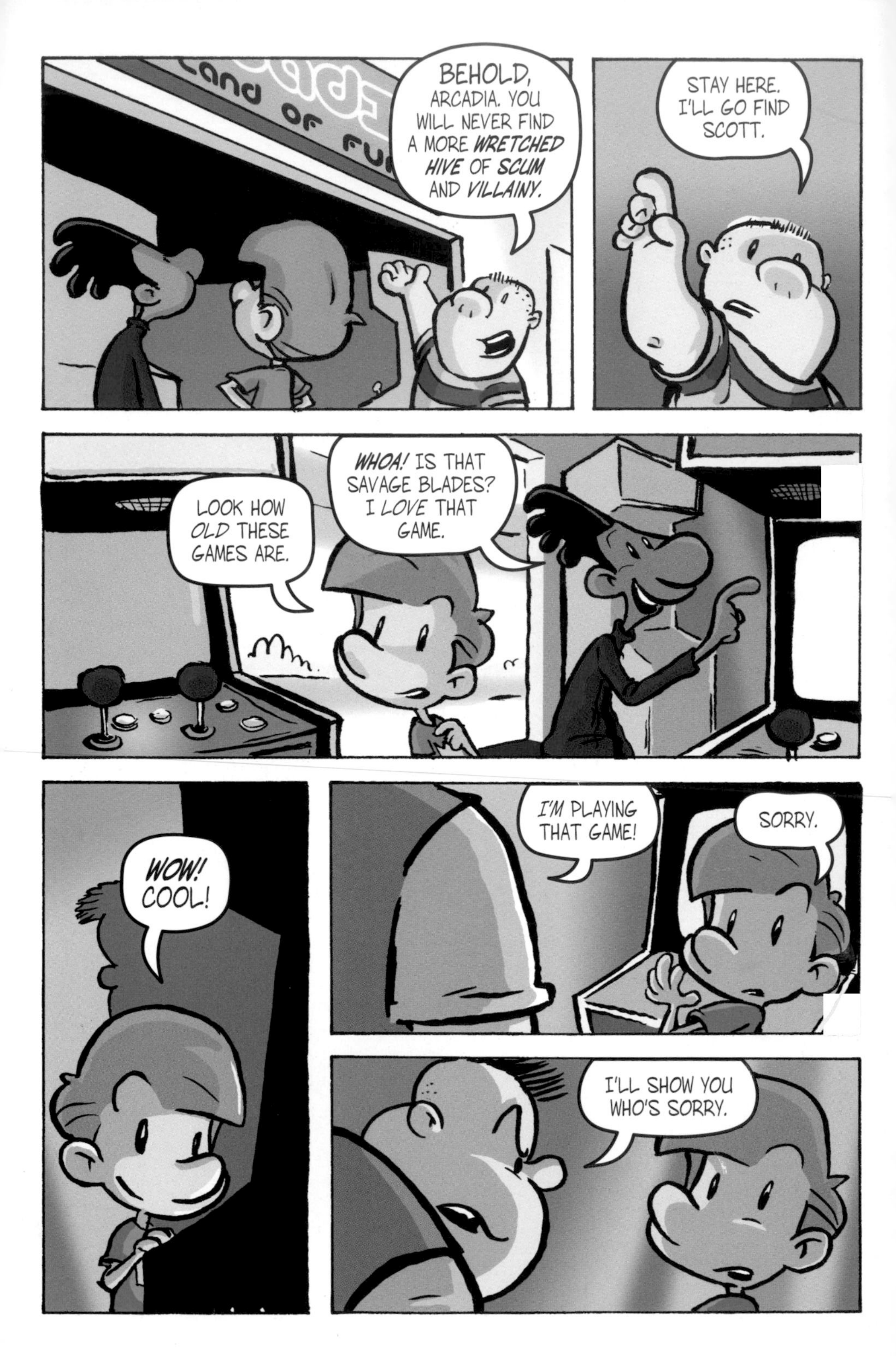
LAND OF FU
BEHOLD, ARCADIA. YOU WILL NEVER FIND A MORE WRETCHED HIVE OF SCUM AND VILLAINY.
STAY HERE. I'LL GO FIND SCOTT.
LOOK HOW OLD THESE GAMES ARE.
WHOA! IS THAT SAVAGE BLADES? I LOVE THAT GAME.
WOW! COOL!
I'M PLAYING THAT GAME!
SORRY.
I'LL SHOW YOU WHO'S SORRY.

NO FIGHTING IN ARCADIA.
SORRY, ANGUS. I WAS JUST LEAVING.
I AM THE GAME-KEEPER.
YOUR FRIEND TELLS ME YOU WISH TO SEE SCOTT.
YES, WE'D LIKE TO . . .
THERE IS ONLY ONE WAY TO SEE SCOTT. YOU FIRST DEFEAT HIS CHAMPION.
WHO'S THAT?
ME.
arcadia
ANGUS
DEFEAT YOU? I THOUGHT THERE WAS NO FIGHTING IN . . .
NOT FIGHTING. YOU MUST BEST ME IN MY FAVORITE GAME.
Land of Fun
SAVAGE BLADES.
SAVAGE BLADES
INSERT COINS

SAVAG
BLAD
I ACCEPT YOUR CHALLENGE.
YOU DO?
SPLENDID, CHALLENGER PAYS.
YOU REALIZE THIS GUY IS THE GAMEKEEPER OF ARCADIA?
I KNOW THAT!
TOK
I PLAYED THIS GAME EVERY DAY LAST SUMMER WHEN I VISITED MY GRANDMOTHER IN FLORIDA. TRUST ME.
CHANGE
I DO.
LET'S DO THIS!
LET'S BEGIN, SHALL WE.

PLAYER
1
PLAYER
2
KLANG
THIS IS *TOO* EASY.

THINK AGAIN, MULLET BOY.
YOU'LL PAY FOR THAT!
BRING IT ON!

KLING
YOU'VE LOST YOUR BLADE. *SURRENDER!*

NEVER!
YEAH
AW, NUTS.
YOU'RE GOOD.
WAIT HERE.

PHLEM THRO
YOU DID IT!!
IT WAS NOTHING.
SCOTT WILL SEE YOU NOW.
FISHING KING
DON'T TOUCH ANYTHING.
PRIVATE
DRAGON WAGONS
WOW! LOOK AT THE GAME TOKENS. THERE MUST BE HUNDREDS.
THOUSANDS!

EXIT
WHO DARES ENTER MY LAIR? WHAT DO YOU WANT?
SODA
SODA
SODA
SODA
LET ME DO THE TALKING.
OH, GREAT AND POWERFUL SAVAGE, WE COME HERE AS FRIENDS. WE . . .
DO I KNOW YOU?
YEAH, KINDA. I'M WAYNE KOZLOWSKI. YOU KNOW MY BROTHER GARETH.
KOZ IS YOUR BROTHER?
YEAH!

I HATE KOZ! KOZ BROKE MY BIKE!
IDIOT, I TOLD YOU WE SHOULD . . .
SILENCE!
WHO ARE YOU? WHAT DO YOU WANT FROM ME?
UH, EXCUSE ME, MR. SAVAGE . . . I'M ARTIE KING. WE'D LIKE YOUR HELP BEATING THIS GROUP OF BULLIES CALLED THE HORDE.
YOU WANT MY HELP? WHAT'S IN IT FOR ME?
UH, WE CAN PAY YOU. I'VE GOT $10 BIRTHDAY MONEY FROM MY GRANDMOTHER. AND SOME COMIC BOOKS.
WHAT DO I WANT WITH $10 AND COMIC BOOKS?
WELL, THAT'S ALL I HAVE.
THEN YOU HAVE NOTHING. BEGONE!

OK, THANKS.
BUMP
SORRY ABOUT THAT. . .
PICK THEM UP!
WE JUST HAVE A FEW MORE.

HURRY UP!
SOME ROLLED BEHIND THE GAME.
ALMOST THERE.
I GOT IT! SORRY FOR THE TROUBLE. WE'LL BE . . .
WAIT A MINUTE! MAYBE YOU DO HAVE SOMETHING I NEED.
REALLY?

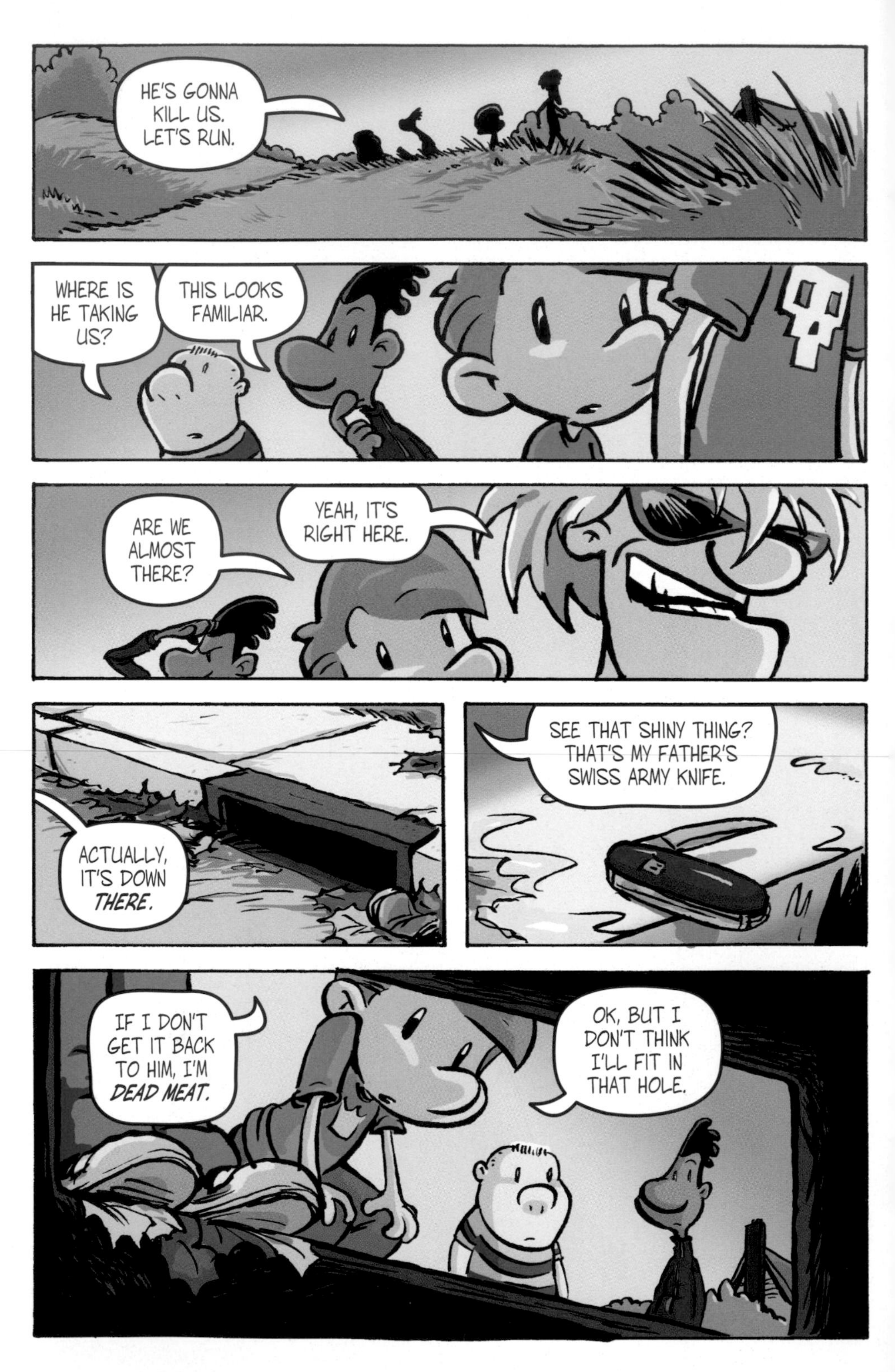
HE'S GONNA KILL US. LET'S RUN.
WHERE IS HE TAKING US?
THIS LOOKS FAMILIAR.
ARE WE ALMOST THERE?
YEAH, IT'S RIGHT HERE.
ACTUALLY, IT'S DOWN *THERE*.
SEE THAT SHINY THING? THAT'S MY FATHER'S SWISS ARMY KNIFE.
IF I DON'T GET IT BACK TO HIM, I'M *DEAD MEAT*.
OK, BUT I DON'T THINK I'LL FIT IN THAT HOLE.

NO, YOU CAN'T FIT IN *HERE*, BUT I BET YOU'LL FIT OVER *THERE.*
DOWN THE RAVINE YOU WILL FIND A CULVERT. IT'S BARRED BUT I THINK YOU ARE SMALL ENOUGH TO FIT THROUGH.
GO IN THERE AND BRING BACK MY FATHER'S KNIFE, AND I'LL DEFEAT THE HORDE SINGLE-HANDEDLY. YOU HAVE MY WORD.
NOW I KNOW WHERE WE ARE. WE'RE NEAR . . .
HOOOWLLL
THE *BEAST!*

THAT'S WHERE THE BEAST LIVES. DON'T DO IT.
I HAVE TO OR THE HORDE WILL BEAT US TO A PULP.
DIDN'T SOME KID DISAPPEAR DOWN HERE?
FORGET SCOTT. WE'LL FIND SOMEONE ELSE FOR OUR TEAM.
LIKE WHO? GWEN? NOT LIKELY.
YOU'LL THANK ME FOR THAT LATER.
BUT WHAT ABOUT THE BEAST? IT COULD KILL YOU.
I THOUGHT YOU SAID THERE'S NO SUCH THING.

THERE'S A BIGGER DRAIN ALONG THE WAY. I'LL GET THE KNIFE AND GET OUT THERE.
LOOK ON THE BRIGHT SIDE . . .
. . . IF YOU GET *EATEN*, WE WON'T HAVE TO PLAY DODGEBALL!

OW!

THERE IT IS!

GOT IT!
HOOWWLL
HUH?
WHOA!
AAHHHHHH

GRRRRRR
GRRRR

GRRRRRRRR
EASY, BOY.
I KNOW . . .
DOGGIE SNACKS
IT'S OK. HERE YOU GO. *GOOD BOY.*

WE BETTER CALL 911.
ARTIE?
SORRY ABOUT YOUR FRIEND. LET ME KNOW ABOUT CALLING HOURS!
HEY! DON'T YOU WANT YOUR KNIFE BACK?
YOU'RE ALIVE!
WHERE'D YOU GET THE DOG?
BOYS, MEET THE BEAST. POOR THING WAS STUCK DOWN THERE.
HERE'S YOUR KNIFE. IT'S GOT DOG SLOBBER ON IT.

ARTIE, THANKS, I OWE YOU. I WILL HELP YOU DEFEAT THE HORDE. I SWEAR ALLEGIANCE TO YOU AND YOUR FRIENDS. YOU WILL NOT LOSE THAT GAME, THIS I PROMISE.
EUGENE SCOTT SAVAGE! GET IN THE CAR THIS INSTANT!
MA!?
I'VE BEEN LOOKING ALL OVER TOWN FOR YOU.
AWW, MA, I WAS . . .
EUGENE?
SEE, IT'S LIKE I SAID: NOTHING TO IT.
WITH THE COMBINATION OF MY BRAINS AND YOUR SKILLS, WE'LL GO PLACES.
YEAH, LIKE THE GRAVEYARD.

ARTIE, WHERE HAVE YOU BEEN? ARE YOU ALL RIGHT? WHAT IS *THAT?*
I'M OK, I JUST FELL DOWN.
HIS NAME IS ***BEAST.*** I RESCUED HIM. CAN WE KEEP HIM?
EWW! NO WAY AM I SHARING THE HOUSE WITH ANOTHER ***FILTHY ANIMAL.***
MORGAN, BE NICE.
IT'S NOT FAIR! HOW CAN YOU LET HIM HAVE A DOG WHEN HE STEALS MY THINGS?
I DON'T HAVE YOUR ***DUMB*** DIARY!
MORGAN
LIAR!
SO, CAN WE KEEP HIM?
A DOG IS A LOT OF RESPONSIBILITY.

NO WAY! IT'S EITHER THE DOG OR ME.
MORGAN
NICE KNOWING YOU.
GRRRRR!
WHAT IS IT, BOY? HEY, LOOK! HE FOUND MORGAN'S DIARY!
IT WAS IN MORGAN'S BACKPACK ALL ALONG.
YOU PROBABLY PUT IT THERE.
WELL, THIS DOG HAS COME IN HANDY ALREADY.
THAT MEANS WE CAN KEEP HIM?
OK, BUT YOU BOTH NEED A BATH.

FRIDAY
MR. MERLYN, YOU'RE LEAVING?
I'VE GOT TO RUN HOME AND CHANGE. DON'T WORRY, I WON'T MISS THE DODGEBALL LEGEND IN ACTION.
YEAH, WELL, I'M NOT REALLY A . . .
I KNOW.
YOU DO?
DIDN'T I TELL YOU? I'M YOUR WISE AND POWERFUL GUIDANCE COUNSELOR? I KNOW ALL.
HAVE YOU TOLD WAYNE AND PERCY YET?
NO, I'M SCARED. WHAT IF I TELL THEM AND THEY STOP TALKING TO ME?

MR. MERLYN, I'M SORRY. I'VE RUINED EVERYTHING!
JUST MY LUCK THAT STUPID LOCKER HAD TO OPEN FOR ME.
DO YOU REALLY BELIEVE THAT OPENING THE LOCKER WAS JUST LUCK?
ARTHUR, YOU ARE SPECIAL. YOU'VE GOT THE RIGHT COMBINATION.
RAAWK, DUMB LUCK.
IT WAS THERE ON THE DOOR.
I'M NOT TALKING NUMBERS. I'M TALKING ABOUT WHAT'S INSIDE YOU. NO ONE HAS BEEN ABLE TO OPEN THAT LOCKER FOR AGES. THEN, YOU COME ALONG AND WHAM! BANG! YOU CAN OPEN IT UP. I CALL THAT SPECIAL.
AND I'M NOT ALONE, PERCY AND WAYNE THINK IT'S SPECIAL.
HECK, EVEN JOE ROMAN THINKS SO.

YEAH, RIGHT.
HELLO??? EARTH TO ARTHUR! ISN'T THAT WHY YOU'RE PLAYING JOE IN DODGEBALL?
BUT IT'S JUST A DUMB LOCKER! IT DOESN'T GIVE ME WHAT I WANT! IT ONLY GIVES ME TROUBLE!
DID YOU EVER THINK THAT MAYBE IT ONLY GIVES YOU WHAT YOU NEED?
BIRD FEED
I DON'T GET IT.
FIGURE IT OUT. I DID TELL YOU THAT YOU'D BE TESTED THIS WEEK.
SEE YOU AT THE GAME, ARTHUR KING OF CORNWALL.

SECRET SECRETARY TO QUEEN MEANIE, THE OWL HAS LEFT THE NEST. OVER.
MISS FLUNKE? IS THAT YOU?
ROGER, I THOUGHT WE OUGHT TO USE CODE NAMES. OVER.
OF COURSE YOU DID. WHAT'S GOING ON?
THE OWL IS LEAVING. OVER.
EXCELLENT, YOU KNOW WHAT TO DO.
ROGER THAT. OVER AND OUT.

YOU SEEN SCOTT YET?
IT'S ALMOST FOUR.
DUDE, HE SAID HE'D BE HERE.
YO! ARTIE!
ANGUS, AM I EVER GLAD YOU GUYS ARE HERE.
WHERE'S SCOTT?
SCOTT CAN'T MAKE IT. HE'S GROUNDED. HIS FATHER FOUND OUT HE TOOK THE KNIFE. HE SAYS HE'S SORRY.
I *KNEW* IT!
BUT SCOTT TOLD ME TO GIVE YOU A TOKEN OF HIS GRATITUDE. HE SAYS YOU ARE ALWAYS WELCOME IN ARCADIA.
GEE, THANKS.
WHAT IS IT?
A TOKEN.
arcadia Land of Fun

HEY, WAIT! WHERE ARE YOU GOING? CAN YOU PLAY DODGEBALL?
I'D LOVE TO, BUT I CAN'T.
I'M GAMEKEEPER OF ARCADIA. FRIDAY IS OUR BIGGEST NIGHT. SORRY.
aracdia
ANGUS
VICTORY, DUDES.
IT'S ALMOST GAME TIME. WHO ARE WE GONNA GET TO BE OUR FOURTH?
THERE'S ALWAYS . . .
DON'T SAY IT!
HOW ABOUT YOUR BROTHER, GARETH?
YOU KIDDING ME?
I HAVEN'T EVEN TOLD HIM ABOUT HIS GAME BOY YET.
SO WHERE ARE WE GOING TO FIND SOMEONE NOW?
GIRLS LOCKER ROOM

MEANWHILE
JOSEPH.
HULLO, MRS. DAGGER, YOU WANTED TO SEE ME?
I NEED YOU TO WIN THIS GAME TODAY.
WE WILL, MRS. DAGGER, WE WILL.
WOULDN'T IT BE NICE IF YOUR OPPONENTS HAD TO FORFEIT?
I GUESS SO, BUT I'D RATHER SMASH THEM TO PIECES.
IT'S NOT THAT I DON'T TRUST YOUR ABILITIES, BUT I'D LIKE YOU TO TRY AND MAKE SURE THOSE CRETINS NEVER STEP FOOT ON THE DODGEBALL COURT. IS THAT UNDERSTOOD?
YEAH, BUT WHAT ABOUT THE SMASHING?
AM I UNDERSTOOD, JOSEPH?
YES, MRS. DAGGER.

WHAT HAS HAPPENED TO MR. MERLYN?
WHY DID WE GET THE GIRLS' LOCKER ROOM?
I BET MRS. DAGGER IS BEHIND THIS.
HELLO, GENTLEMEN. THE GAME STARTS IN FIFTEEN MINUTES. YOU KNOW THAT IF YOU DO NOT HAVE FOUR PLAYERS YOU WILL HAVE TO FORFEIT.
YOU ALSO WILL NEED GYM CLOTHES, WHICH I SEE YOU HAVE.
WHAT ABOUT MR. MERLYN?
IF HE'S NOT HERE IN TIME, WE'LL START WITHOUT HIM. HE'S PROBABLY SEEN YOUR CHANCES AND HAS ALREADY DECIDED TO LEAVE.

WE'RE SO DEAD. WE'RE DEADER THAN DEAD.
WE WOULDN'T BE IF IT WASN'T FOR YOU AND YOUR STUPID GAME BOY!
HEY, YOU'RE THE JERK WHO CHALLENGED THE HORDE IN THE FIRST PLACE.
ME? WHAT ABOUT THAT DUMB TRIP TO ARCADIA?
WE GOT SCOTT TO HELP US.
WHERE IS HE NOW?
AT LEAST I'M DOING SOMETHING! YOU JUST. . .
STOP! IT'S NOT YOUR FAULT! IT'S MY FAULT.
NO IT'S NOT. YOU'RE OUR ONLY CHANCE AT WINNING.
YOU'RE THE DODGEBALL LEGEND.
NO I'M NOT!

WHAT?!?
IT'S A LIE!
I'M NOT A DODGEBALL LEGEND. I MEAN I AM, BUT NOT IN A GOOD WAY. I'M A LEGEND AT BEING BAD. I STINK AT DODGEBALL!
WHY DID YOU TELL US YOU WERE SUCH A CHAMP?
I JUST WANTED TO FIT IN. I WAS AFRAID IF I SAID I STUNK AT DODGEBALL YOU WOULDN'T BE MY FRIENDS.
I'M SORRY. I'LL GO TALK TO MRS. DAGGER.
IF YOU WANT TO QUIT, I UNDERSTAND.

QUIT? ARE YOU KIDDING?
AFTER ALL WE'VE BEEN THROUGH?
NO WAY! YOU MAY STINK AT DODGEBALL, BUT WE'RE IN THIS TOGETHER. BESIDES, YOU'RE STILL THE CHOSEN GUY WITH THE LOCKER.
AS MUCH AS I HATE TO SAY IT, HE'S RIGHT. YOU'RE THE CHOSEN GUY.
THANKS, GUYS.
WE STILL DON'T HAVE A FOURTH PLAYER.
THERE'S GWEN?
UH-UH, I DON'T WANT . . .
GET OVER IT! SHE MAY NOT BE THE PLAYER YOU WANT. BUT SHE'S THE PLAYER WE NEED!

WHAT DID YOU SAY?
I SAID...
NEVER MIND. WAYNE, GO BEG GWEN TO PLAY FOR OUR TEAM.
NO! NEVER!
I...OK.
PERCY, GO LOOK FOR MR. MERLYN.
WHERE ARE YOU GOING?
I LEFT SOMETHING IN MY LOCKER.

SKIDDDDD
WHERE DO YOU THINK YOU'RE GOING? RUNNING AWAY? OH, NO YOU DON'T. GET BACK TO THAT GYM RIGHT NOW!
SECRET SECRETARY TO QUEEN MEANIE, OVER.
WHAT IS IT, MISS FLUNKE?
THE OWL HAS A FLAT. OVER.

WHAT DO YOU WANT ME TO DO WITH HIS BIKE? OVER.
LEAVE IT. GET BACK HERE AS SOON AS YOU CAN.
001XCL
HEY THERE.

SO THEY STUCK YOU GUYS IN THE GIRLS' LOCKER ROOM. FUNNY.
WAYNE THINKS SO. ANYWAYS, GWEN, THANKS FOR PLAYING.
MY PLEASURE. WHAT'S IN THE LUNCH BAG?
MY SECRET PLAN.
YOU HAVE A SECRET LUNCH PLAN?
ARTIE, YOU SHOULD SEE THIS.
WHAT'S GOING ON?
THE HORDE STOLE OUR GYM CLOTHES. WHAT DO WE DO NOW?
WE ARE SO DEAD. WE'RE DEADER THAN DEAD. WE'RE DECOMPOSING DEAD.
HOLD ON, I'M THINKING.
YOU BOYS FORGET WHERE YOU ARE.

NO WAY! I WILL NOT GO OUT THERE LIKE THIS!
WE DON'T HAVE MUCH CHOICE, THE GAME IS ABOUT TO BEGIN.
THEY'RE HUGE!
THEY'RE PINK!
THEY SAY "KNIGHTS PLUMBING & HEATING."
MY DAD SPONSORS A WOMEN'S SOFTBALL TEAM. THEY PRACTICE IN THE SCHOOL FIELD AND USE THESE LOCKERS.
IT LOOKS LIKE WE'RE WEARING DRESSES.
Knights PLUMBING & HEATING
I PREFER "TUNIC."
WE'RE ROADKILL DEAD.
REALLY, YOU GUYS, IT'S NOT THAT BAD.
SHE'S RIGHT. AND DON'T FORGET: I HAVE A PLAN!

LADIES AND GENTLEMEN, WELCOME TO CAMELOT MIDDLE SCHOOL FOR THIS VERY SPECIAL DODGEBALL GAME. TODAY TWO TEAMS ENTER THE FIELD OF BATTLE. AND ONLY ONE WILL LEAVE AS WINNERS.
INTRODUCING THE REIGNING CHAMPIONS. THE SCOURGE OF THE SCHOOL YARD, THE HORROR OF THE HALLS, THE MASTERS OF DISASTER, THE HORDE!
HORDE SMASH!

AND NOW, THE CHALLENGERS: THEY'RE LEAN, THEY'RE MEAN, THEY'RE SQUEAKY CLEAN, THEY'RE THE KNIGHTS!
GO GEEKS!
CAPTAINS, PLEASE MEET IN CENTER COURT.
7
2
3

GENTLEMEN, YOU KNOW THE RULES. IF ANYONE IS HIT BY A BALL, HE IS OUT.
POW
IF ANYONE CATCHES A THROWN BALL, THE PERSON WHO THREW THE BALL IS OUT.
BALLS THROWN AT THE HEAD WILL RESULT IN THE PERSON WHO THREW THE BALL BEING CALLED OUT.
WAP
AND LASTLY, IF A BALL HITS A REF, THE PERSON WHO THREW IT IS OUT.
GENTLEMEN, SHAKE HANDS. LET'S MAKE IT QUICK.

SO, WE'RE CALLED THE KNIGHTS?
I GUESS SO.
1, 2, 3, GO KNIGHTS!
THE PLAYERS TAKE THE COURT.
THE GAME HAS BEGUN!
TWEET

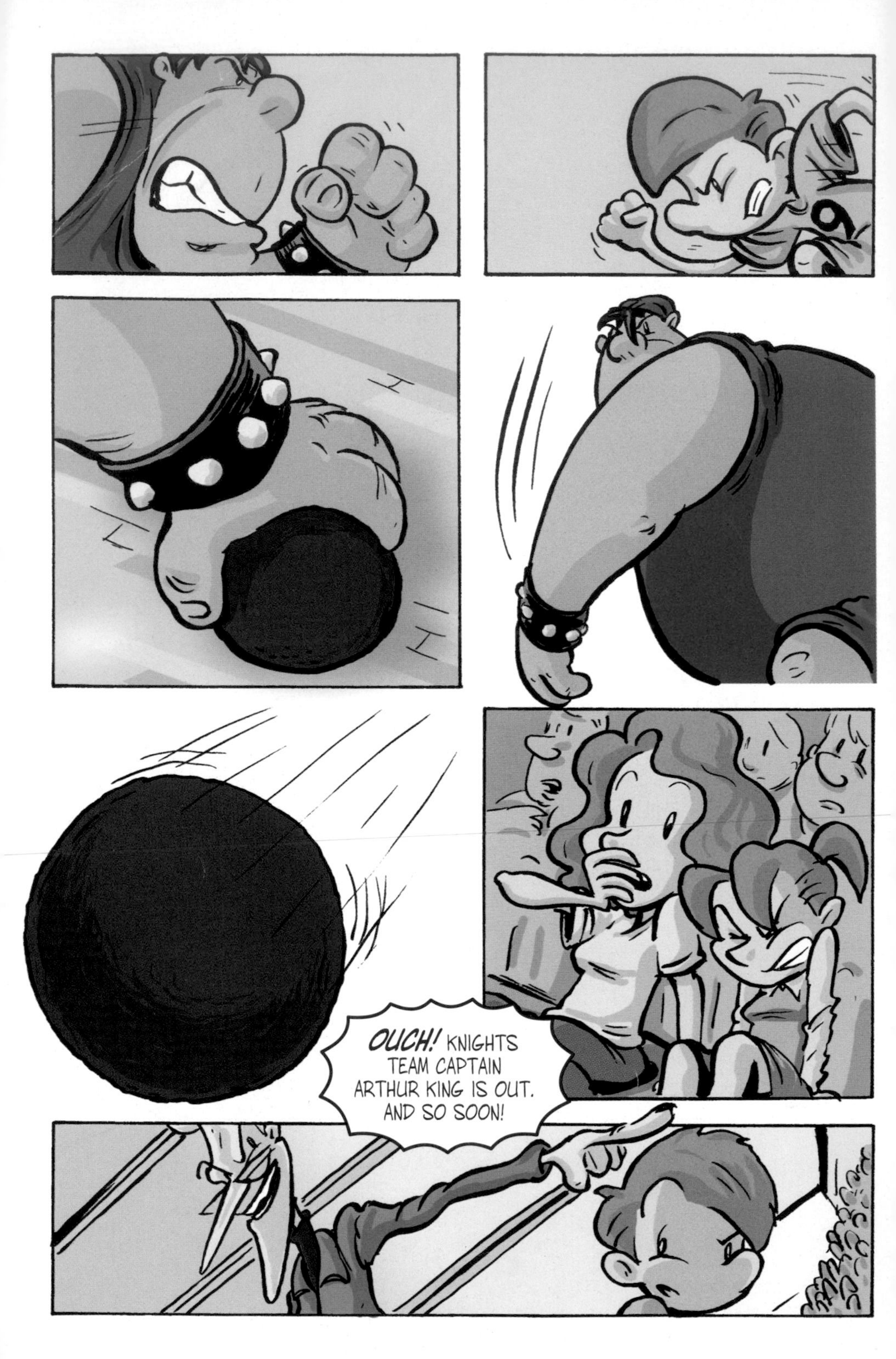
OUCH! KNIGHTS TEAM CAPTAIN ARTHUR KING IS OUT. AND SO SOON!

GREAT CATCH BY GWEN LEE! HORDEMAN STEWART MONK IS OUT!
OH, THAT HURT. DWAYNE FERRYMAN IS OUT! THE HORDE ONLY HAS TWO PLAYERS LEFT.
ARTHUR KING IS BACK IN.
OOH, NOT SO FAST!

ARTHUR KING IS *OUT* AGAIN.
LOOK AT THOSE MOVES BY PERCIVAL JONES!
WAY TO GO, PERCY!
THANK YOU.
WHOA! HE'LL FEEL THAT IN THE MORNING.

THE HORDE IS TEAMING UP ON GWEN NOW. IT DOESN'T LOOK GOOD FOR THE KNIGHTS.
STAY BEHIND ME. MOVE WHEN I MOVE.
NOW!
WAYNE KOZLOWSKI HAS BEEN HIT IN THE HEAD. JOE ROMAN SHOULD BE OUT.
HEY! HE HIT ME IN THE HEAD.
DON'T BE A CRYBABY.
UNBELIEVABLE! THE REF IS CALLING KOZLOWSKI OUT! GWEN LEE IS LEFT THERE ALONE. WHAT ARE THE KNIGHTS GOING TO DO?
Knights
PLUMBING & HEATING

TIME-OUT!
GWEN, YOU'RE DOING A GREAT JOB!
I NEED YOU TO GET ME BACK IN THERE.
IT'S RISKY. I'LL HAVE TO PUT THE BALL DOWN AND TRY TO CATCH ANOTHER ONE.
WHAT IS SHE DOING?
GWEN LEE HAS PUT DOWN THE BALL. THIS IS SUICIDE.

OH, NO! THEY ARE SETTING HER UP FOR THE HORDE DOUBLE SMASH.
GWEN CATCHES IT! BUT IT WAS A TRICK! JOE STILL HAS HIS BALL.
GWEN! LOOK OUT!
WHAM

IT'S NOT OVER YET. THE ONCE AND FUTURE DODGEBALL KING ARTIE IS BACK IN!
HE MUST PLAN ON BEING ON THE COURT FOR A WHILE. LOOKS LIKE HE BROUGHT HIS LUNCH.
WELL, IF IT ISN'T THE TOUGH GUY WHO THINKS HE RULES THE SCHOOL?
NOT QUITE THE LEGEND, ARE YOU, KING?
GO ON, TRY TO PICK UP THE BALL. WHAT'S WRONG? SCARED?

SOON, THE LOCKER WILL BE MINE!
ACTUALLY, I FOUND SOMETHING IN THERE YOU MIGHT LIKE TO SEE.
WHAT'S THAT? ANOTHER ONE OF YOUR SOAP SANDWICHES?
SAY HELLO TO MY LITTLE FRIEND.

WHAT'S WRONG? AFRAID OF A LITTLE SPIDER?
AAAAHHHH
JOE ROMAN HAS FLIPPED! HE'S THROWN AWAY THE BALL AND IT'S HEADING FOR MRS. . . .
BONK

TWEET
YOU'RE OUT! YOU HIT A REF. KNIGHTS WIN!
THE KNIGHTS WIN! THE KNIGHTS WIN!
ISN'T THAT GREAT! YEAH, ARTIE!
JUST WONDERFUL.

NOT BAD FOR A GIRL, HUH?
HANNIBAL! I MISSED YOU.
SORRY I'M LATE. BIKE TROUBLE. GOOD THING I KNOW A SHORTCUT.
GO AWAY!
ARTIE ARTIE

MONDAY
WHAT ARE YOU *LAUGHING* AT?
HEE-HEE-HEE-HEE
STOP LAUGHING!
DETENTION FOR YOU!
AND *YOU* . . .
AND *YOU* . . .
YOU . . .
AND *YOU* . . .
WHO WANTS TO PLAY DODGEBALL?

RAAWK, HAIL TO THE KING!
INDEED, OBERON, INDEED.
WHAT IS THAT?
WHAT DOES IT LOOK LIKE?
DON'T YOU EVER LEARN?
I NEED THIS, FOR STUDY HALL.
ARTIE, COMING TO LUNCH?
I'LL MEET YOU THERE.

COOL, PEANUT BUTTER AND JELLY!

HELLO?

THANK YOU.

001 XCL
THE END. . . FOR NOW.

Dodgeball legend Frank Cammuso is a three-time recipient of the Wedgie. He has also received the prestigious Noogie and the Hurtz Donut.

Cammuso is the Eisner-nominated creator of the Max Hamm, Fairy Tale Detective graphic novels. He draws political cartoons for *The Post-Standard* and his work has appeared in *Newsweek*, *The New York Times*, *The Washington Post*, and *USA Today*. He lives with his wife in Syracuse, New York.